BoE 7035

C000204862

Hi
Session

100 SONGS YOU REALLY SING

BOSWORTH EDITION

INHALT/CONTENTS

A HARD DAY'S NIGHT

Words & Music by John Lennon & Paul McCartney

1.
      C   **F**   **C**   **B♭**   **C**
It's been a hard day's night and I've been working like a dog.
                 F   **C**   **B♭**   **C**
It's been a hard day's night, I should be sleeping like a log.
       F   **G7**   **C F7 C**
But when I get home to you, I find the things that you do will make me feel alright.

2.
      C   **F**   **C**   **B♭**   **C**
It's been a work all day to get you money to buy you things
                 F   **C**   **B♭**   **C**
And it's worth it just to hear you say you're gonna give me ev'rything.
       F   **G7**   **C F7 C**
So why on earth should I moan, 'cause when I get you alone you know I'll be okay.

        Em **Am**   **Em**
Zw.: When I'm home ev'rything seems to be alright,
          C **Am**   **F** **G7**   **C**
when I'm home feeling you holding me tight, tight, yeah. It's been a hard ...

ALL MY LOVING

♩ 176 Beat

Close your eyes and I'll kiss you, to-mor-row I'll miss you;
tend that I'm kiss-ing the lips I am

miss you; re-mem-ber I'll al-ways be true.___
miss-ing and hope that my dreams will come true.___

___ And then while I'm a-way, I'll write home ev'-ry

day___ and I'll send all my lov-ing___ to you.___ I'll pre-

___ All my lov-ing___ I will send to you.___

___ All my lov-ing___ dar-ling,___ I'll be true.___

Words & Music by John Lennon and Paul McCartney
© 1963 Northern Songs. All Rights Reserved. International Copyright Secured.

1.
       Em   **A**   **D**   **Bm**
    Close your eyes and I'll kiss you, tomorrow I'll miss you;
    G   **Em**   **C A**
    remember I'll always be true.
       Em   **A**   **D**   **Bm**
    And then, while I'm away, I'll write home ev'ry day,
    G   **A**   **D**
    and I'll send all my loving to you.

2.
       Em   **A**   **D**   **Bm**
    I'll pretend that I'm kissing the lips I am missing
      G   **Em**   **C A**
    and hope that my dreams will come true.
       Em   **A**   **D**   **Bm**
    And then, while I'm away, I'll write home ev'ry day,
    G   **A**   **D**
    and I'll send all my loving to you.

      Bm **F#**   **D**   **Bm** **G**   **A7**   **D**
Ref.: All my loving I will send to you. All my loving, darling, I'll be true.

5

A HORSE WITH NO NAME

♩ 122 | Shuffle

On the first part of the jour-ney I was look-ing at all the life, there were plants and birds and rocks and things, there were sand and hills and rings. The first thing I met was a fly with a buzz and the sky with no clouds, the heat was hot and the ground was dry, but the air was full of sound. I've been through the des-ert on a horse with no name, it felt good to be out of the rain, in the des-ert you can re- mem-ber your name, 'cause there ain't no one for to give you no pain.

La la la la la la la la la la.

2x D.C.,
2.x fade out

Words & Music by Dewey Bunnell
© by Warner Brothers Music Ltd.,
für D/A/CH: Neue Welt Musikverlag GmbH, München
(WARNER/CHAPPELL MUSIC GMBH GERMANY)

      Em   D   Em   D

1. On the first part of the journey I was looking at all the life,

          Em   D

there were plants and birds and rocks and things,

          Em   D

there were sand and hills and rings.

```
        Em                    D                        Em            D
The first thing I met was a fly with a buzz and the sky with no clouds,
        Em                    D                        Em            D
the heat was hot and the ground was dry, but the air was full of sound.

            Em                          D
Ref.: I've been through the desert on a horse with no name,
            Em                    D
    it felt good to be out of the rain,
            Em                  D
    In the desert you can remember your name,
                Em              D
    'cause there ain't no one for to give you no pain.
Em   D          Em D Em   D          Em D
La la la la la la la la la la la. La la la la la la la la la la la.
```

8 Takte Instrumental Break

```
        Em              D              Em                  D
2.  After two days in the desert sun my skin began to turn red,
            Em                      D
    after three days in the desert fun was looking at a river bed.
                Em              D
    And the story is told of a river that flowed
                Em              D
    made me sad to think it was dead.
```

Ref.: I've been through the desert on a horse with no name ...

```
        Em              D                      Em                  D
3.  After nine days I let the horse run free 'cause the desert had turned to sea.
                Em                  D
    There were plants and birds and rocks and things,
                Em                  D
    there were sand and hills and rings.
        Em              D                      Em                  D
    The ocean is a desert with its life underground and the perfekt disguise above.
            Em          D                      Em                  D
    Under the cities lies a heart made of ground, but the humans will give no love.
```

Ref.: I've been through the desert on a horse with no name ...

    ... La la la la la la la la la la la. La la la la la la la la la la la. *(4x, fade out)*

ALL RIGHT NOW

♩ | 120 | Beat

There she
stood in the street, smil - ing from her head to her feet. I said
"Hey, what is this?" Now ba - by, may-be, may-be she's in need of a
kiss. I said "Hey, what's your name, ba - by, may-be we can see things the
same. Now don't you wait or he - si - tate, let's move
be - fore they raise the park - ing rate." All right
now, ba - by, it's all right now. All right
now, ba - by, it's all right now.
All right now, ba - by, it's all right now.

repeat and
fade out

Words & Music by Paul Rodgers & Andy Fraser
© 1970 blue Mountain Music Limited, 8 Kensington Park Road, London W11
All Rights Reserved. International Copyright Secured.

```
   C                    F   C    F                          C
1. There she stood in the street, smiling from her head to her feet.
                      F   C              F                      C
   I said "Hey, what is this?" Now baby, maybe she's in need of a kiss.
                      F   C              F                          C
   I said "Hey, what's your name, baby, maybe we can see things the same.
                      F   C              F                              C
   Now don't you wait or hesitate, let's move before they raise the parking rate."
           F      Bb        F        C
Ref.:  All right now, baby, it's all right now.
           F      Bb        F        C
       All right now, baby, it's all right now.

   C                    F   C    F                          C
2. I took her home to my place, watching ev'ry move on her face.
                      F   C              F                          C
   She said "Look, what's your game, baby, are you tryin' to put me in shame?"
                      F   C              F                    C
   I said "Slow, don't go so fast, don't you think that love can last?"
                      F   C   F                          C
   She said "Love, Lord above, now you're tryin' to trick me in love."
           F      Bb        F        C
Ref.:  All right now, baby, it's all right now.
           F      Bb        F        C
       All right now, baby, it's all right now.
           F      Bb        F        C
       All right now, baby, it's all right now ... (fade out)
```

9

ALL YOU NEED IS LOVE

2x D.S.
2.x repeat
Ref. + fade out

Words & Music by John Lennon & Paul McCartney
© 1967 Northern Songs

```
       G    D    Em   G    D    Em   Am   G    D
     Love, love, love. Love, love, love. Love, love, love.
     G                          D                Em    D7
1.   There's nothing you can do that can't be done.
     G                D              Em    D7
     Nothing you can sing that can't be sung.
     Am                                                      D7
     Nothing you can say, but you can learn how to play the game, it's easy.

     G                          D              Em   D7
2.   There's nothing you can make that can't be made.
     G               D              Em    D7
     Nothing you can save that can't be saved.
     Am                                                     D7
     Nothing you can do, but you can learn how to be you in time, it's easy.

     G         A7    D7 G        A7    D7
Ref.: All you need is love,  all you need is love,
     G         B7    Em  G  C      D7      G
     all you need is love, love,  love is all you need.

     G                          D              Em   D7
3.   There's nothing you can know that isn't known.
     G              D              Em    D7
     Nothing you can see that isn't shown.
     Am                                                     D7
     Nowhere you can be that isn't where you're meant to be, it's easy.

     G         A7    D7 G        A7    D7
Ref.: All you need is love,  all you need is love,
     G         B7    Em  G  C      D7      G
     all you need is love, love,  love is all you need.
     G         A7    D7 G        A7    D7
     All you need is love,  all you need is love,
     G         B7    Em  G  C      D7      G        D7
     all you need is love, love,  love is all you need, love is all you need ...
                                                      (fade out)
```

ALL YOU ZOMBIES

♩ 86 | Slow Rock

Ho - ly Mo - ses met the Pha - raoh, yeah, he tried to set him
straight. Looked him in the eye: let my people go.
Ho - ly Mo - ses on the moun - tain,
high a - bove the gol - den calf, went to get the Ten Command - ments,
he's just gon-na break them in half. All you Zom-bies hide your
fa - ces, all you peo-ple in the street. All you sit-tin' in high
pla - ces, the pie-ces gon-na fall on you.
liv-ing all by them-selves. You don't have to hide a - ny-more!
All you Zom-bies hide your fa - ces,
all you peo-ple in the street. All you sit-tin' in high

pla - ces,   the pie-ces gon na fall on you.—

(repeat and fade out)

Words & Music by Rob Hyman & Eric Bazilian
© by Human Boy Music & Dub Notes,
für D/A/CH: Neue Welt Musikverlag GmbH, München
(WARNER/CHAPPELL MUSIC GMBH GERMANY)

Gm   Dm   F   C Gm   Dm   C
1. Holy Moses met the Pharaoh,   yeah, he tried to set him straight.
Gm   Dm Gm   A7 Dm
   Looked him in the eye: let my people go!
Gm   Dm   F   C Gm   Dm   C
   Holy Moses on the mountain,   high above the golden calf,
Gm   Dm   F   C Gm   Dm   C
   went to get the Ten Commandments,   he's just gonna break them in half.

Gm   Dm   F C Gm   Dm   C
Ref.: All you zombies hide your faces,   all you people in the street.
Gm   Dm   F   C Gm   Dm   Gm Dm
   All you sittin' in high   places,   the pieces gonna fall on you.

Gm   Dm   F C Gm   Dm   C
2. No one ever spoke to Noah,   they all laughed at him instead;
Gm   Dm Gm   A7 Dm
   working on his ark,   working all by himself.
Gm   Dm   F   C Gm   Dm   C
   Only Noah saw it coming,   forty days and forty nights.
Gm   Dm   F   C Gm   Dm   C
   Took his sons and daughters with him,   they were the Israelites!

Gm   Dm   F C Gm   Dm   C
Ref.: All you zombies hide your faces,   all you people in the street.
Gm   Dm   F   C Gm   Dm   Gm Dm
   All you sittin' in high   places,   the rain's gonna fall on you.

Gm   Dm   F   C Gm   Dm   C
3. Holy father, what's the matter?   Where have all your children gone?
Gm   Dm   A7
   Sittin' in the dark, living all by themselves,
                       Dm
   You don't have to hide anymore!

Gm   Dm   F C Gm   Dm   C
Ref.: All you zombies hide your faces,   all you people in the street.
Gm   Dm   F   C Gm   Dm
   All you sittin' in high   places,   the pieces gonna fall on you.
Gm   Dm   F C Gm   Dm   C
   All you zombies hide your faces,   all you people in the street.
Gm   Dm   F   C Gm   Dm
   All you sittin' in high   places,   it's all gonna fall on you.

13

ALWAYS LOOK ON THE BRIGHT SIDE OF LIFE

♩ 120 | Medium Beat

Some things in life are bad, they can real-ly make you mad, oth-er things just make you swear and curse. When you're chewing on life grist-le, don't grum-ble, give a whist-le and this-'ll help things turn out for the best. And al-ways look on the bright side___ of life,___ (gepfiffen) al-ways look on the light side___ of life.___ ___ (gepfiffen) If life seems jol-ly rot-ten there's some-thing you've for-got-ten and that's to laugh and smile and dance and sing. When you're feel-ing in the dumps don't be sil-ly chumps, just purse your lips and whist-le, that's the thing! And you And al-ways look on the bright side___ of life.___ (gepfiffen) repeat and fade out

Words & Music by Eric Idle

```
        D7          Am              A°           G              Em
Intr.: Some things in life are bad, they can really make you mad,
        Am                D7                 G
       other things just make you swear and curse.
                    Am                 D7            G              E
       When you're chewing on life's gristle, don't grumble, give a whistle
         A                A7                D
       and this'll help things turn out for the best.

       D7 G       Em            Am   D7     G   Em Am D7
1.     And always look on the bright side of life,
         G      Em          Am  D7    G   Em Am D7
       always look on the light side of life
        Am              D7              G                  Em
       If life seems jolly rotten, there's something you've forgotten
           Am                 D7                G
       and that's to laugh and smile and dance and sing.
         Em          Am           D7       G           Em
       When you're feeling in the dumps, don't be silly chumps,
             A               A7               D
       just purse your lips and whistle, that's the thing!

       D7 G       Em            Am   D7     G   Em Am D7
2.     And always look on the bright side of life,
         G      Em          Am  D7    G   Em Am D7
       always look on the light side of life
           Am           D7           G            Em
       For life is quite absurd and death's the final word,
                  Am               D7              G
       you must always face the curtain with a bow.
      Em  Am            D7            G           Em
       Forget about your sin, give the audience a grin,
             A               A7             D
       enjoy it, it's your last chance anyhow!

       D7 G        Em            Am   D7    G   Em Am D7
3.     So  always look on the bright side of death,
         G      Em          Am      D7         G   Em Am D7
       just before you draw your terminal breath.
        Am              D7      G          Em
       Life's a piece of shit, when you look at it,
       Am                D7               G
       life's a laugh and death's a joke, it's true.
       Em  Am            D7             G             Em
       You'll see it's all a show, keep 'em laughin' as you go,
             A               A7              D
       just remember that the last laugh is on you.

       D7 G       Em            Am   D7     G   Em Am D7
       And always look on the bright side of life,
         G      Em          Am  D7    G   Em Am D7
       always look on the right side of life.          (repeat and fade out)
```

15

AMERICAN PIE

♩ | 120 | Shuffle

A long, long time a-go— I can still re-mem-ber how that mu-sic used to make me smile. And I knew— if I had my chance that I could make those peo-ple dance and may-be they'd be hap-py— for a while. But Fe-bru-a-ry made me shiv-er with ev'-ry pa-per I de-liv-er bad news on the door-step, I could-n't take one more step. I can't re-mem-ber if I cried when I read a-bout his wi-dowed bride,— some-thing touched me deep in-side— the day the mu-sic died. So bye, bye, Miss A-me-ri-can Pie. Drove my Che-vy to the la-vy but the la-vy was dry.— Them good ole boys— were drink-ing whis-key and rye,— sing-ing

this will be the day_ that I_ die,_ this will be the day that I_ die._

_ Did you write the book of love_ and do you_ have faith in

God a-bove if the bib-le tells_ you so?_ Now, do

you be-lieve in Rock'n'Roll,_ can mu-sic save your mor-tal soul_ and

can you teach me how to dance real slow?_____ Well, I

know that you're in love with him, 'cause I saw you danc-ing in the gym, you

both kicked off your shoes, man, I dig those rhy-thm and

blues._____ I was a lone - ly teen - age bronk-ing buck_ with a

pink car-na - tion and a pick-up truck, but I knew I was out_ of luck_ the day

_ the mu - sic died. I start-ed sing-ing:

4x D.S.
4.x al ✪-✪

_ sing-ing: this will be the day_ that I_ die._

Words & Music by Don McLean
© 1971 Music Corporation of America Inc. & Benny Bird Company Inc., USA
Universal/MCA Music Limited, 77 Fulham Palace Road, London W6
All Rights Reserved. International Copyright Secured.

```
         G    D   Em    Am              C               Em
1.  A long, long time ago I can still remember how that music
                    D
    used to make me smile.
         G         D        Em     Am                  C
    And I knew if I had my chance that I could make those people dance
         Em          C          D
    and maybe they'd be happy for a while.
              Em     Am              Em       Am
    But February made me shiver with ev'ry paper I deliver
     C      G     Am      C          D
    bad news on the doorstep, I couldn't take one more step.
         G     D        Em       Am        D
    I can't remember if I cried, when I read about his widowed bride,
         G       D       Em         C        D7    G
    Something touched me deep inside the day the music died.  So

         G  C          G      D
Ref.:  Bye, bye, Miss American Pie.
                  G         C        G        D
       Drove my Chevy to the lavy but the lavy was dry.
                  G       C         G       D
       Them good ole boys were drinking whiskey and rye,
                Em                      A  Em                        D
       singing this will be the day that I die, this will be the day that I die.

    G                  Am              C            Am
2.  Did you write the book of love and do you have faith in God above
    Em
       if the bible tells you so?
    D      G    D    Em        Am             C
    Now, do you believe in Rock 'n' Roll, can music save your mortal soul
    Em                 Am              D
    and can you teach me   how to dance real slow?
              Em           D              Em           D
    Well, I know that you're in love with him, 'cause I saw you dancing in the gym,
           C        G      Am      C            D7
    you both kicked off your shoes, man, I dig those rhythm and blues.
           G     D     Em              Am            C
    I was a lonely teenage bronking buck with a pink carnation and a pick-up truck,
       G    D    Em        C     D7   G C G       D7
    but I knew I was out of luck the day the music died. I started singing: (Ref.)

           G                 Am              C            Am
3.  Now for ten years we've been on our own and moss grows fat on a rolling stone,
       Em        D
    but that's not how it used to be.
              G    D       Em              Am          C
    When the jester sang for the king and queen in a coat he borrowed from
                  Em     Am           D
    James Dean and a voice that came from you and me.
              Em           Am           Em           D
    Oh, and while the king was looking down the jester stole his thorny crown,
       C      G   Am     C               D7
    the courtroom was adjourned, no verdict was returned.
           G    D    Em          Am          C
    And while Lenin read a book on Marx, the quartet practiced in the park
       G    D    Em        C     D7   G C G       D7
    and we sing dirges in the dark the day the music died. We were singing: (Ref.)
```

     G   Am   C   Am

4. Helter-skelter in the summer swelter, the birds flew off with a fall-out shelter

  Em   D

  eight miles high and falling fast.

      G   D Em   Am   C

  It landed foul on the grass, the players tried for a forward pass

           Em   Am   D

  with the jester on the sidelines in a cast.

          Em   D   Em   D

  Now the half-time air was sweet perfume, while sergeants played a marching tune

  C   G   Am   C   D7

  we all got up to dance, oh, but we never got a chance.

                G   D Em   Am   C

  'Cause the players tried to take the field, the marching band refused to yield.

  G   D   Em   C   D7 G C G   D7

  Do you recall what was revealed the day the music died. We started singing: (Ref.)

      G   Am   C   Am

5. Oh, and there we were all in one place, a generation lost in space

      Em   D

  with no time left to start again.

            G   D Em   Am   C

  So come on, Jack, be nimble, Jack, be quick. Jack Flash sat on a candlestick,

        Em   Am   D

  'cause fire is the devil's only friend.

Em   D   Em   D

  And as I watched him on the stage, my hands were clenched in fists of rage,

  C   G   Am   C   D7

  no angel born in hell could brake that Satan's spell.

                G   D Em   Am   C

  And as the flames climbed high into the night to light the sacrificial rite,

      G   D   Em   C   D7 G C G   D7

  I saw Satan laughing with delight the day the music died. We were singing: (Ref.)

  G   D   Em   Am   C

6. I met a girl who sang the blues and I asked her for some happy news,

      Em   D

  but she just smiled and turned away.

  G   D   Em   Am   C

  I went down to the sacred store, where I'd heard the music years before,

        Em   Am   D

  but the man there said the music wouldn't play.

      Em   Am   Em   Am

  And in the streets the children screamed, the lovers cried and the poets dreamed.

      C   G   Am   C   D7

  But not a word was spoken, the church bells all were broken.

          G   D   Em   Am   D

  And the three men I admire most, the Father, Son and Holy Ghost,

      G   D   Em   C   D7   G

  they caught the last train for the coast the day the music died.

                 D7   G C   G   D

  And they were singing: Bye, bye, Miss American Pie ...

          Em   A Em   D

  ... singing this will be the day that I die, this will be the day that I die,

     C   D7   G

  singing this will be the day that I die.

ALWAYS

Words & Music by Jon Bon Jovi
© 1994 Jon Bon Jovi Publishing / Universal Music Publishing Limited, 77 Fulham Palace Road, London W6
All rights reserved. International Copyright secured

```
    C#m                        B
1.  This Romeo is bleeding   but you can't see his blood,
    A                              G#m
    it's nothing but some feelings that this old dog has kicked up.
    C#m                                    B
    It's been raining since you left me, now I'm drowning in the flood,
    A                              G#m         A  B
    you see I've always been a fighter, but without you I give up.
    C#m                        B
    Now I can't sing a love song like the way it's meant to be,
              A                          B          A  B
    well, I guess I'm not that good anymore, but baby that's just me.  Yeah,

        E    B      F#m C#m B    E           B          A  C#m B
Ref.: I will love you baby,    al-ways and I'll be there for ever and a day, al-ways.
      E                                      B
      I'll be there till the stars don't shine, till the heavens burst

      and the words don't rhyme,
                    A                          B      A  B  C#m
      I know when I die, you'll be on my mind and I'll love you al- ways.


    C#m                                    B
2.  Now your pictures that you left behind are just memories of a different life.
    A
    Some that made us laugh, some that made us cry
    G#m
    One that made you have to say goodbye.
    C#m
    What I'd give to run my fingers through your hair,
         B
    to touch your lips, to hold you near.
    A
    When you say your prayers, try to understand,
        G#m                      A  B
    I've made my mistakes, I'm just a man.
    C#m
    When he holds you close, when he pulls you near,
           B
    when he says the words you've been needing to hear,
         A
    I wish I was him 'cause those words are mine
         B                    A  B
    to say to you till the end of time.     Refrain


      D                  G        A     D           G        A
Zw.: If you told me to cry for you, I could. If you told me to die for you, I would.
     Bm        A       G                    A
     Take a look at my face, there's no price I won't pay to say these words to you.
     B        A
     Well, there ain't no luck in these loaded dice
              B
     but baby, if you give me just one more try,
            A
     we can pick up our old dreams and our old lives,
            B      E       A        B
     we'll find a place where the sun still shines yeah,     Refrain
```

22

BAD MOON RISING

♩ 88 | Country Beat

I see the bad＿ moon＿ ri-sing, I see＿ trou-ble on the way. I see＿ burnt＿ wakes of light-ning, I see＿ bad＿ times a-head. Don't call round to-night,＿ they're bound to take your bag.＿ There's a bad moon on the rise. rise. Well, don't come round to-night,＿ well it's bound to take your bag,＿ there's a bad moon on the rise.

Words & Music by John Cameron Fogerty

    D   **A7 G D**   **A7 G**   **D**
1. I see the bad moon rising, I see trouble on the way.
         A7 G   **D**   **A7 G**   **D**
I see burnt wakes of lightning, I see bad things ahead.
  G   **D**   **Bm**
Ref.: Don't call round tonight, they're bound to take your bag.
   A7   **G**   **D**
There's a bad moon on the rise.
   D   **A7 G**   **D**   **A7**   **G**   **D**
2. I hear hurricanes ablowing, I know the end is.coming soon.
         A7 G   **D**   **A7**   **G**   **D**
I feel rivers overflowing, I hear the voice of rack and ruin.   *Refrain*
   D   **A7 G**   **D**   **A7**   **G**   **D**
3. Hope you got your things together, hope you can grab a bag today!
         A7   **G**   **D**   **A7**   **G**   **D**
Looks like we're in for hasty weather, well, now you're thinking for a nap.
  G   **D** **D7 G**
Ref.: Don't call round tonight ... on the rise. Well, don't come round tonight,
      D   **Bm A7**   **G**   **D**
it's bound to take your bag, there's a bad moon on the rise.

BASKET CASE

♩ 166 | Beat

Do you have the time to lis-ten to me whine a-
bout noth-ing and ev-'ry-thing all at once?

I am one of those mel-o-dra-ma-tic fools; neu-
ro-tic to the bone, no doubt a-bout it.

Some-times I give my-self the creeps.

Some-times my mind plays tricks on me. It
all keeps add-ing up. I think I'm crack-ing up.

Am I just par-a-noid? Am I just stoned?

Grasp-ing to con-trol so I bet-ter hold on.

(3x wdh.)

Words & Music by Billie Joe Armstrong / Frank E. Wright / Mike Pritchard
© by Green Daze Music & WB Music Corp.
für D/A/CH: Neue Welt Musikverlag GmbH, München
(WARNER/CHAPPELL MUSIC GMBH GERMANY)

```
         D             A      Bm           F#m
1.   Do you have the time to listen to me whine
         G             D                A
     about nothing and ev'rything all at   once?
     D             A      Bm           F#m
     I am one of those melodramatic fools;
          G           D                        A
     neurotic to the bone, no doubt about it.

       G              A           D
Ref.:  Sometimes I give myself the  creeps.
       G              A             D
       Sometimes my mind plays tricks on  me.
         G          A       D        C      Bm
       It all keeps adding up, I think I'm cracking up.
          G        A           D     A Bm A D A Bm A
       Am I just paranoid? Am I just stoned?

         D             A      Bm           F#m
2.   I went to a shrink to analyze my dreams.
             G           D                  A
     She says it's lack of sex that's bringing me   down.
         D        A      Bm           F#m
     I went to a whore, she said my life's a bore,
          G           D                          A
     so quit my whining 'cause it's bringing her down.

       G              A           D
Ref.:  Sometimes I give myself the  creeps.
       G              A             D
       Sometimes my mind plays tricks on  me.
         G          A       D        C      Bm
       It all keeps adding up, I think I'm cracking up.
          G        A           D     A Bm A D A Bm A
       Am I just paranoid? Am I just stoned?
```

Instrumental break

```
       G              A           D
Ref.:  Sometimes I give myself the  creeps.
       G              A             D
       Sometimes my mind plays tricks on  me.
         G          A       D        C      Bm
       It all keeps adding up, I think I'm cracking up.
          G        A           D      (Bm G D A)4x  G D A
       Am I just paranoid? Am I just stoned?
```

BECAUSE I LOVE YOU

♩ 79 | Slow Beat

Be-cause I love you, oh,_____ to be my light, to be my

guide._____ I got you a let - ter from the

post - man the o - ther day,_____ so I de - ci - ded to write this song__

just to let you know ex - act - ly the way I feel,_____

to let you know___ my love's for real._____ Be-cause I love you and

I'll do a - ny - thing.__ I give you my heart,____ my

ev' - ry - thing. Be-cause I love you I'll be right by__ your side___

to be your light, to be your guide._____ Be-cause I

love you my heart's an o - pen door.__ Oh, won't you please

come on in.__ Be-cause I love you I'll be right by__ your side___

to be your light,___ to be your guide._____

26

If you should feel___ that I don't real-ly care___

and that you're start - ing to lose ground,___

just let me re-as-sure you___ that you can count___ on me___

and that I'll al - ways be a-round   Be-cause I

D.S.
and fade

Words & Music by Warren Allen Brooks
© 1990 by SHR Publ. Co.,
für D/A/CH: MUSIKVERLAG INTERSONG GMBH, Hamburg

```
         C   G  C G Em      B7            E
Because I love you, oh,    to be my light, to be my guide.
Em          B7                        Em
1. I got you a letter from the postman the other day,
        B7            E
   so I decided to write this song
Em             D   G         C
   just to let you know exactly the way I feel,
Em        B7              E
   to let you know my love's for real.
     Em         C  D    C       G Em          B    Em
Ref.: Because I love you and I'll do anything. I give you my heart, my ev'rything.
                C   D    C          G Em     B7              E
      Because I love you, I'll be right by your side, to be your light, to be your guide.
Em           B       B7        Em
2. If you should feel that I don't really care
                 B7          E
   and that you're starting to lose ground,
Em              B7                      Em
   just let me reassure you that you can count on me
              B7         E
   and that I'll always be around.

Ref.: Because I love you ...
     Em         C  D    C         G Em            B    Em
Because I love you, my heart's an open door. Oh, won't you please come on in.
                C   D   Bm          Em        B7              E
Because I love you, I'll be right by your side, to be your light, to be your guide.

If you should feel ... Because I love you ... (fade out)
```

BLAZE OF GLORY

♩ 76 | Slow-Rock

I wake up in the morn - ing and I raise my wear-y head.___ I've got an old coat for a pil-low and the earth was last - night's bed. I don't know where I'm go-ing, on - ly God knows where I've been. I'm a dev-il on the run,___ a six - gun lov-er, a can - dle in___ the wind, yeah!

You seen it die___ in vain. Shot down in a blaze of glo - ry, take me now but know the truth. 'Cause I'm go-ing down in a blaze of glo - ry. Lord, I nev-er drew first but I drew first blood, I'm the de-vil's son call me Young Gun. Each night I go to bed, I pray the Lord my soul to keep. No I ain't look-ing for for-give - ness but be -

Gm
fore I'm six-feet deep, Lord,

B♭
I got to ask a fa-vour and I

F
hope you'll un-der-stand. 'Cause I've lived life to the full-est,

C
let this boy

Gm
die like a man.

C
Star-ing down a bul-let, let me make

Gm
my fin-al stand.

Shot

D.S. al 𝄏-𝄏

C
no one's son, call me Young Gun.

G

F
I'm a Young Gun.

C
Young Gun,

G
yeah, yeah, yeah Young

F

C
Gun.

G

3

Words & Music by Jon Bon Jovi

```
       Gm                          F
1.  I wake up in the morning and I raise my weary head.
                 C                          Gm
    I've got an old coat for a pillow and the earth was last night's bed.
        Bb                       F
    I don't know where I'm going, only God knows where I've been.
             C                          G              D
    I'm a devil on the run, a six-gun lover, a candle in the wind, yeah!
       Gm                          F
    You ask about my conscience and I offer you my soul.
                 C                          Gm
    You ask, if I'll grow to be a wise man, well, I ask if I'll grow old.
        Bb                                  F
    You ask me if I've known love and what it's like to sing songs in the rain.
             C                          Gm
    Well, I've seen love come, I've seen it shot down, I've seen it die in vain.
            C              G              C              G
Ref.: Shot down in a blaze of glory, take me now, but know the truth.
                        C              G
      'Cause I'm going down in a blaze of glory.
            F                       F
      Lord, I never drew first, but I drew first blood,
            C                       G
      I'm the devil's son, call me Young Gun.
            Gm                          F
Zw.: Each night I go to bed, I pray the Lord my soul to keep.
                 C                          Gm
     No, I ain't looking for forgiveness, but before I'm six feet deep,
         Bb                       F
     Lord,  I got to ask a favour and I hope you'll understand.
             C                          Gm
     'Cause I lived life to the fullest, let this boy   die like a man.
          C                    Gm
     Staring down a bullet, let me make my final stand.
            C              G                          F
Ref.: Shot down in a blaze of glory ... but I drew first blood,
                  C                          G  F           C G
      and I'm no-one's son, call me Young Gun.  I'm a Young Gun.
                  F                       C G
      Young Gun, yeah, yeah, yeah Young Gun.
                  Gm                          F
2.  When you're brought into this world, they say you're born to sin.
            C                          Gm
    Well, at least they gave me something I didn't have to steal or have to win.
        Bb                       F
    Well, they tell me that I'm wanted, yeah, I'm a wanted man.
          C              G              D
    I'm a colt in your stable, I'm what Cain was to Abel,
            Gm
    Mister, catch me if you can.

            C              G
Ref.: Shot down in a blaze of glory ...




30
```

BARBARA ANN

♩ 184 | Rock 'n' Roll

Bar-bara Ann, Bar - bar-bara Ann. Bar-bara Ann, Bar - bar-bar Bar-bara

Ann,_____ take__ my hand,_____ Bar-bara Ann,

— you got me rock-in' and a-roll-in', rock - in' and a-reel-in', Bar-bara

Ann, Bar-bar-bar - bar-bara Ann. (Fine) Went to a dance look-in' for ro-mance,

saw Bar-bara Ann, so I thought I'd take a chance. Bar-bara Ann,

take__ my hand,_____ you got me rock-in' and a-roll-in', rock-

in' and a-reel-in', Bar-bara Ann, Bar-bar-bar - bar-bara Ann.

2x D.C.
2.x al Fine

Words & Music by Fred Fassert
© 1961 Longitude Music Co., USA
Windswept Pacific Music Limited, Hope House, 40 St. Peter's Road, London W6

G
Intr.: Barbara Ann, Barbarbara Ann, Barbara Ann, Barbarbara Ann.

     G   **C**   **G**   **D7**
Ref.: Barbara Ann take my hand, Barbara Ann, you got me rockin' and a-rollin',
     C   **G**
     rockin' and a-reelin', Barbara Ann, Barbar-barbarbara Ann.

     G
1.   Went to a dance lookin' for romance, saw Barbara Ann,
                                   C   **G**
    so I thought I'd take a chance. Barbara Ann, take my hand ... *Intro + Ref.*
     G
2.   Played my fav'rite tune, danced with Betty Lou, tried Peggy Sue,
                                   C   **G**
    but I knew they wouldn't do. Barbara Ann, take my hand ... *Intro + Ref.*

BREATHLESS

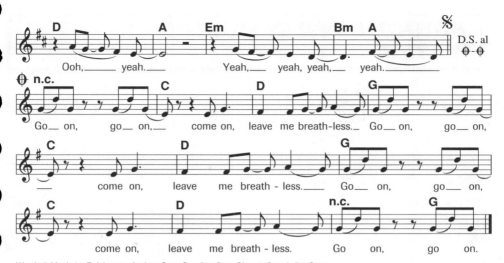

    n.c.   **D**   **A**   **Em Bm A**
   Go on. Go on, leave me breathless. Come on. Ooh, yeah.

    D   **A**   **Em**   **Bm**   **A**
1.   The daylight's fading slowly,   but time with you is standing still.
    D   **A**   **Em**   **Bm**   **A**   **G**
   I'm waiting for you only,   the slightest touch and I feel weak.
   A   **Bm7**   **G**   **A**   **D**   **G**   **A**   **Bm7**
   I cannot lie, from you I can not hide. And I'm losing the will to try.
          G   **A**
   Can't hide it, can't fight it. So

        G   **C**   **D**
Ref.: Go on, go on, come on, leave me breathless.
     G   **C**   **D**   **G**   **C**
   Tempt me, tease me until I can't deny this loving feeling.
         D   **G**   **C** **D**   **A**   **Em Bm A**
   Make me long for your kiss. Go on, go on. Yeah, come on. Ooh, yeah.

   D   **A**   **Em**   **Bm**   **A**
2.   And if there's no tomorrow   and all we have is here and now,
   D   **A**   **Em**   **Bm**   **A**   **G**
   I'm happy just to have you.   You're all the love I need somehow.
   A   **Bm7**   **G**   **A**   **D**   **G**   **A**   **Bm7**
   It's like a dream, although I'm not asleep and I never want to wake up.
       G   **A**
   Don't lose it, don't leave it. So

Ref.: Go on, go on, come on, leave me breathles ... Yeah, come on.
  A   **Em Bm A D**   **A Em**   **Bm**   **A**
   Yeah, yeah.   Ooh, yeah.   Yeah, yeah, yeah, yeah. I cannot lie ...
     D   **E**   **C**   **D**
   ... long for you kiss.   Go on, go on, com on, leave me breathless. *(3x)*
  n.c.   **G**
   Go on, go on.

33

BRIDGE OVER TROUBLED WATER

♩ 88 | Ballade

1. When you're wea - ry, feel - in' small, when tears are in your eyes, I'll dry them all; I'm on your side. Oh,___ when times get rough___ and friends just can't be found, ___ like a bridge o - ver trou - bled wa - ter I will lay me down. Like a bridge o - ver trou - bled wa - ter I will lay me down.

2. When you're trou - bled wa - ter I will lay me down. ___

D.S. al

3. Sail on

bridge o - ver trou - bled wa - ter I will ease your mind.

___ Like a bridge o - ver trou - bled wa - ter I will ease your mind.

Words & Music by Paul Simon
© 1969 Paul Simon
All Rights Reserved. International Copyright Secured.

```
      C          G   C          G   C
1.  When you're weary,  feelin' small,
          F   C  G      C        G      C  G C G
    when tears are in your eyes, I'll dry them all;
        D  Em  D                      G   G7
    I'm on your side. Oh, when times get rough
                    C    A D
    and friends just can't be found,
```

```
     G  G7 C       G      E7  C    B7    Em
Ref.: Like a bridge over troubled water  I will lay me down.
     G  G7 C       G      E7  C    D7    G    C G C G
    Like a bridge over troubled water  I will lay me down.
```

```
      C          G            C              G  C
2.  When you're down and out,  when you're on the street,
          F   C  G      C          G      C  G C G
    when evening falls so hard I will comfort you.
        D  Em  D                     G    G7
    I'll take your part. Oh, when darkness comes
                    C  A D
    and pain is all around,
```

```
     G  G7 C       G      E7  C    B7    Em
Ref.: Like a bridge over troubled water  I will lay me down.
     G  G7 C       G      Em  C    Em B Em
    Like a bridge over troubled water  I will lay me down.
```

A7 G C Em C Cm G C G C G C

```
            G        C      G C
3.  Sail on Silver girl,  sail on by.
          F   C  G      C          G            C   G C G
    Your time has come to shine. All your dreams are on their way.
        D  Em  D                 G       G7
    See how they shine. Oh, if you need a friend
                    C    A D
    I' sailing right behind,
```

```
     G  G7 C       G      Em  C    Em B  Em
Ref.: Like a bridge over troubled water  I will ease your mind.
     G  G7 C       G      Em  C    B7      Em A7 G C Cm G
    Like a bridge over troubled water  I will ease your mind.  Oh
```

35

BLOWIN' IN THE WIND

 ♩ 84 Beat

How man-y roads must a man walk down, be - fore you can call him a man?__ Yes 'n' how man-y seas must a white dove sail be - fore she can sleep in the sand? Yes 'n' how man-y times must the can - non - ball fly be - fore they for-e - ver are banned? The ans - wer, my friend, is blow-in' in__ the wind, the ans - wer is blow-in' in the wind._____

Words & Music by Bob Dylan
© 1962 M. Witmark & Sons, USA
renewed 1990 Special Rider Music, USA - This arrangement © 2000 Special Rider Music
All Rights Reserved. International Copyright Secured.

1. How many roads must a man walk down, before you can call him a man?
    Yes 'n' how many seas must a white dove sail, before she can sleep in the sand?
    Yes 'n' how many times must the cannon ball fly, before they forever are banned?
Ref.: The answer, my friend, is blowin' in the wind, the answer is blowin' in the wind.

2. How many times must a man look up, before he can see the sky?
    Yes 'n' how many ears must one man have, before he can hear people cry?
    Yes 'n' how many deaths will it take till he knows that too many people have died? *Ref.*

3. How many years can a mountain exist, before it is washed to the sea?
    Yes 'n' how many years can some people exist, before they're allowed to be free?
    Yes 'n' how many times can a man turn his head and pretend that he just doesn't see? *Ref.*

36

BYE BYE LOVE

♩ 160 | Swing

Words & Music by Felice & Boudleaux Bryant

```
   E              B  B7       E              B  B7        E
1. There goes my baby  with someone new.  She sure looks happy,  I sure am blue.
           A      E    A       E            A              B7          E
   She was my baby till he stepped in. Good-bye to romance    that might have been.
       A     E  A       E        A        E              B7   E
Ref.: Bye-bye love, bye-bye happiness,  hello loneliness, I think I'm gonna cry.
       A   E  A     E          A     E              B7     E
   Bye-bye love, bye-bye sweet caress,  hello emptiness, I feel like I could die.
       B7       E
   Bye-bye, my love, bye-bye.

   E              B  B7          E                         B  B7       E
2. I'm through with romance, I'm through with love, I'm through with counting the stars above.
                 A         B7      F#m      B7          E
   And here's the reason that I'm so free: My lovin' baby is through with me. Refrain
```

37

CALIFORNIA DREAMING

All the leaves are / All the leaves are brown and the sky is grey___ and the sky is grey.
brown

I've been for a / I've been for a walk on a win-ter's day
walk

on a win-ter's day.___ I'd be safe and I'd be safe and warm
warm___

if I was in L. A.___ if I was in L. A.___ Ca-li-for-nia

Ca-li-for-nia dream - in' on such a win-ter's day.___
dream - in'

Stopped in-to a church I passed a-long___ the way;

well I get down on my / Get down on my knees,___ and I pre-tend to pray
knees

and I pre-tend to pray,___ you know the prea-cher likes the

prea - cher likes the cold,___ he knows I'm gon-na stay___
cold,

knows I'm gon-na stay.___ Ca-li-for-nia Ca-li-for-nia dream-
dream - in'

38

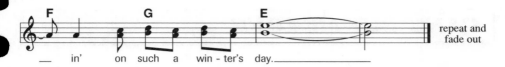

              in'   on   such   a   win - ter's day.

repeat and
fade out

Words & Music by John Phillips & Michelle Phillips
© 1965, 1966 Wingate Music Corporation, USA
Universal/MCA Music Limited, 77 Fulham Palace Road, London W6
All Rights Reserved. International Copyright Secured.

              Am   G   F
              All the leaves are brown
All the leaves are brown
         G   E
and the sky is grey - and the sky is grey.
F   C   E   Am
             I've been for a walk
I've been for a walk
        F   E
on a winter's day - on a winter's day.

             Am   G   F
            I'd be safe and warm,
I'd be safe and warm,
      G   E
if I was in L. A. - if I was in L. A.

          Am G   F   G   E
           California dreamin' on such a winter's day.
California dreamin'   on such a winter's day.
          Am G F   E
Stopped into a church,   I passed along the way;
F   **C   E   Am**
              Get down on my knees,
well, I get down on my knees,
        F   E
and I pretend to pray - and I pretend to pray,
                    Am   G   F
                  preacher likes the cold,
you know the preacher likes the cold,
         G   E
he knows I'm gonna stay - knows I'm gonna stay.

          Am G   F   G   E
           California dreamin' on such a winter's day.
California dreamin'   on such a winter's day.

(repeat and fade out)

CAN'T BUY ME LOVE

Can't buy me love,_____ oh,____ love_____ oh,____ can't buy me love,_____ oh.____ I'll buy you a dia-mond ring, my friend, if it makes you feel al - right,____ I'll get you an-y-thing, my friend, if it makes you feel al - right.____ 'Cause I don't care too much for mon-ey, for mon-ey can't buy me love.____ I'll ____ Can't buy me love, ____ oh, ev' - ry-bo-dy tells me so.____ Can't buy me love, ____ oh, no no no___ no! Say you don't need no dia - mond rings___ and I'll be sa-tis-fied.____ Tell me that you want the kind ____ of things___ that mon - ey just can't buy.____ I don't care too much for mon-ey, mon-ey can't buy me love._____

D.S. al ⊕-⊕

40

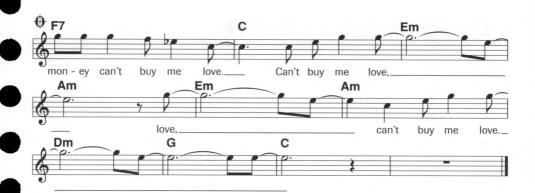

mon - ey can't buy me love.___ Can't buy me love,_____

___ love,_____ can't buy me love.__

Words & Music by John Lennon & Paul McCartney
© 1964 Northern Songs
All Rights Reserved. International Copyright Secured.

       Em Am Em Am   **Dm G**
Can't buy me love, oh, love, oh, can't buy me love, oh.

            C
1.   I'll buy you a diamond ring, my friend, if it makes you feel alright,
      F7   **C**
    I'll get you anything, my friend, if it makes you feel alright.
      G   **F7**   **C**
    'Cause I don't care too much for money, for money can't buy me love.

               C
2.   I'll give you all I've got to give, if you say you love me too,
      F7   **C**
    I may not have a lot to give, but what I've got I'll give to you.
      G   **F7**   **C**
    'Cause I don't care too much for money, for money can't buy me love.

                  Em Am A♭   **G7**   **C**
Ref.: Can't buy me love, oh, ev'rybody tells me so,
                  Em Am Dm   **G**
can't buy me love, oh, no no no no!

         C
3.   Say you don't need no diamond rings and I'll be satisfied.
      F7   **C**
    Tell me that you want the kind of things that money just can't buy.
    G   **F7**   **C**
    I don't care too much for money, money can't buy me love.

4.   *instrumental*

                  Em Am A♭   **G7**   **C**
Ref.: Can't buy me love, oh, ev'rybody tells me so,
                  Em Am Dm   **G**
can't buy me love, oh, no no no no!

     C   **C**
5.   Say you don't need no diamond rings ... money can't buy me love.

               Em Am Em Am   **Dm G C**
Can't buy me love,   love,   can't buy me love.

CANDLE IN THE WIND

♩ 68 | Ballade

C ... **F**
Good-bye Nor - ma Jean___ though I nev-er knew you at all___

C ... **F** ... **C**
___ you had___ the grace to hold your-self___ while those a-round___ you crawled.

F ... **C**
___ They crawled out of the wood-work___

F
and they whis-pered in - to___ your brain,___ they set you___ on a tread-

C ... **F**
mill___ and they made you change your name.___ And it

G7 ... **C**
seems to me___ you lived your life___ like a can - dle in___ the wind,___

F ... **C** ... **Csus4** ... **C**
nev - er know-ing who___ to cling___ to when the rain

G7 ... **F**
___ set in.___ And I would___ have liked___ to have known

Am
___ you but I was just a kid.___ Your can-dle had burned out

G ... **F** ... **C** ... **F**
long be-fore___ your leg-end e - ver did.

C ... **G7** ... **F** ... **C** ... **F** ... **C** ... **G7**

C ... **F**
Good-bye Nor - ma Jean___ though I nev-er knew you at all___

42

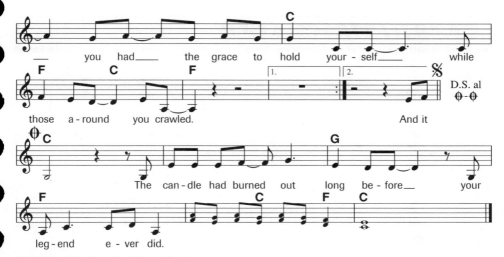

— you had the grace to hold your-self while those a-round you crawled. And it The can-dle had burned out long be-fore your leg-end e-ver did.

Words & Music by Elton John & Bernie Taupin
© 1973 Dick James Music Limited
Universal / Dick James Music Ltd., 77 Fulham Palace Road, London W6.

     C   **F**
1. Goodbye Norma Jean, though I never knew you at all,
                          C   **F** **C**   **F**
    you had the grace to hold yourself, while those around you crawled.
                       C   **F**
    They crawled out of the woodwork and they whispered   into your brain,
                    C   **F**
    they set you on a treadmill and they made you change your name.
        G7   **C**   **F**
Ref.: And it seems to me you lived your life like a candle in the wind,
        C   **Csus4** **C**   **G7**
    never knowing who to cling to,   when the rain set in.
    F   **Am**
    And I would have liked to have known you, but I was just a kid.
                    G   **F**   **C F C G7 F C F C G7**
    Your candle had burned out long before your legend ever did.

     C   **F**
2. Loneliness was tough, the toughest role you ever played.
                       C   **F**
    Hollywood created a superstar and pain was the price you paid.
                  C   **F**
    Even when you died, oh, the press still hounded you,
                   C   **F**
    all the papers had to say was that Marilyn was found in the nude.   Refrain

     C   **F**
Zw.: Goodbye Norma Jean, though I never knew you at all,
                         C   **F** **C**   **F**
    you had the grace to hold yourself, while those around you crawled.
                      C   **F**
    Goodbye Norma Jean, from the young man in the twentysecond row,
                   C   **F** **C**   **F**
    who sees you as something more than sexual, more than just our Marilyn Monroe.
                           G   **F**   **C F C**
Refrain   The candle had burned out long before your legend ever did.

43

CATS IN THE CRADLE

♩ 78 | Rock

My child ar-rived just the oth-er day,

came to the world in the u - su - al way.___ But there were

planes to catch and bills to pay;___ he learned to walk while I

was a-way. he was talk-ing for a mi-nute. And as he grew he'd say:

I'm gon-na be like you, Dad,___ you know I'm gon-na be like

you.___ And the cats in the cra-dle and the sil - ver spoon,

litt - le boy blue and the man___ on the moon. When you com-in' home, son, I

don't know when, we'll get to - geth - er then,___ you

know we'll have a good time then.

1.
Well, my

2.
Well, he

came from col - lege just the oth - er day. so much like a man I just

44

had to say:___ I'm proud of you,___ could you sit for a while? He

shook his head and he said with a smile:___ What I

real - ly like, Dad, is to bor - row the car - keys,

see you la - ter; can I have them please?___ And the

then.

I've long since re - tired; my son's moved a - way,

I called him up just the oth - er day:___ I'd like to see___ you if

you don't mind.___ He said: I'd love to, Dad,___ if I could find the time.___

___ You see, my new job's a has-sle and the kids have the flu.___ But it's

sure nice talk-ing to you, Dad, it's been sure nice talk-ing to you.___

___ And as I hung up the phone it oc - cu - red to me,___ he'd

45

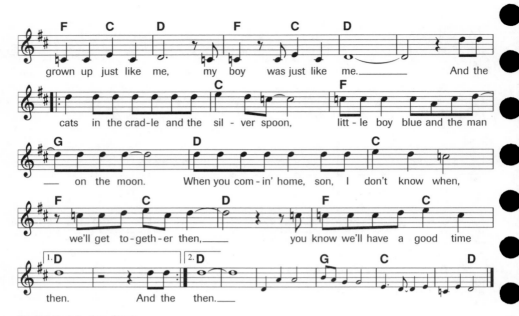

grown up just like me, my boy was just like me._____ And the

cats in the crad-le and the sil - ver spoon, litt - le boy blue and the man

___ on the moon. When you com - in' home, son, I don't know when,

we'll get to-geth-er then,_____ you know we'll have a good time

then. And the then.____

Words & Music by Harry Chapin
© by Story Songs Ltd.

       D   **F**   **G**   **D**
1.   My child arrived just the other day, came to the world in the usual way.
                                 F
      But there were planes to catch and bills to pay;
G   **D**
      he learned to walk, while I was away,
             C
      he was talking for a minute. And as he grew he'd say:
    F   **C**   **D**   **F**   **C**   **D**
    I'm gonna be like you, Dad, you know, I'm gonna be like you.

             D   **C**
Ref.: And the cats in the cradle and the silver spoon,
      F   **G**
      little boy blue and the man on the moon.
     D   **C**
    When you comin' home, son, I don't know when,
F   **C**   **D**   **F**   **C**   **D** **D G C D**
    we'll get together then, you know, we'll have a good time then.

             D   **F**
2.   Well, my son turned ten just the other day,
            G   **D**
      he said: Thanks for the ball, Dad, come on, let's play.
                         F
      Can you teach me how to throw, I said: not today,
          G   **D**
      I've got a lot to do. He said: That's okay
         C
      and he walked away and he smiled and he said you know

```
     F        C     D          F          C     D
I'm gonna be like him, yeah, you know, I'm gonna be like him.
```

Ref.: And the cats in the cradle ...

```
              D                      F
3.   Well, he came from collage just the other day,
            G                D
     so much like a man, I just had to say:
                                   F
     I'm proud of you, could you sit for a while?
            G                  D
     He shook his head and he said with a smile:
                 C
     What I really like, Dad, is to borrow the car-keys,
 F       C         D
     see you later; can I have them, please?
```

Ref.: And the cats in the cradle ...

```
            D                      F
4.   I've long since retired; my son's moved away,
   G                        D
     I called him up just the other day:
                         F
     I'd like to see you, if you don't mind.
                G                    D
     He said: I'd love to, Dad, if I could find the time.
                    C
     You see, my new job's a hassle and the kids have the flu.
              F      C        D            F      C        D
     But it's sure nice talking to you, Dad, it's been sure nice talking to you.
                 C
     And as I hung up the phone, it occured to me,
             F     C      D     F    C        D
     he'd grown up just like me, my boy was just like me.
```

Ref.: And the cats in the cradle ...

```
               D                        C
Ref.:  And the cats in the cradle and the silver spoon,
       F                         G
       little boy blue and the man on the moon.
          D                      C
       When you comin' home, son, I don't know when,
 F          C       D      F              C        D   D G C D
       we'll get together then, you know we'll have a good time then.
```

CECILIA

♩ | 102 | Samba

Ce - lia, you're breaking my heart, you're sha-king my con - fi-dence dai-

ly.___ Oh, Ce - ci - lia, I'm down on my knees, I'm

beg-ging you please to come home.___ Ho - ho - home.

Ma-king love in the af - ter - noon with Ce - ci - lia up in my___

___ bed - room. I got up___ to wash___ my face,___ when I

come back to bed___ some - one's ta - ken my place.___

___ Come on home poh poh poh poh poh poh poh poh poh poh poh poh

___ poh___ Ju - bi - la - tion, she loves me a - gain,___ I

fall on the floor and I'm laugh - ing.___ Ju - bi - - ing.___ Oh oh oh oh oh

oh oh oh oh___ oh oh oh oh oh___ oh oh oh___ oh___ oh oh oh.___ Come on home.

Musik und Text: Paul Simon

```
         E             A            E           A          E          B7
Ref.: ‖:Celia, you're breaking my heart, you're shaking my confidence daily.
              A E       A              E         A            E          B7
      Oh, Cecilia, I'm down on my knees, I'm begging you, please, to come home.:‖
              E
      Ho-ho-home.


                        A
      Making love in the afternoon
              E  A E  B7     E
      with Cecilia up in my bedroom.
                     A
      I got up to wash my face,
                 E                     B7        E
      when I come back to bed, someone's taken my place.

         E             A            E           A          E          B7
Ref.:  Celia, you're breaking my heart, you're shaking my confidence daily.
              A      E       A         E         A            E          B7
      Oh, Cecilia, I'm down on my knees, I'm begging you please to come home.
                    E            A        E         A          B7
      Come on home. Poh poh poh poh poh poh poh poh poh poh poh poh poh.

              A E        A          E   A          E             B7
      ‖:Jubilation, she loves me again, I fall on the floor and I'm laughing.:‖
                A   E    A       E   A      E       B7
      ‖: Oh oh oh oh oh oh oh oh oh oh oh oh oh oh oh oh oh oh. :‖
                E
      Come on home.
```

CITY OF NEW ORLEANS

♩ 148 | Shuffle

1. Ri-ding on the Ci-ty of New Or - leans, Il - li-nois Cen-tral Mon-day morn-ing rail,___ fif - teen cars___ and fif - teen rest-less ri-ders, three con - duc-tors and twen-ty - five sacks of mail.

All out on a south bound od-ys - sey, the train pulls out of Kan-ka-kee, rolls past the hou - ses, farms and fields. Pas - sing towns that have no name and freight yards full of old black men, and the grave - yards of rus - ted au - to - mo - biles. Sing-ing: Good mor - ning A-me - ri - ca, how are___ you? Don't you know that I'm your na - tive son. I'm the train they call the Ci-ty of New Or - leans and I'll be gone five hun - dred miles when the day is done.

Words & Music by Steve Goodman
© 1973 Jurisdad Music & Turnpike Torn Music, USA
Sony/ATV Music Publishing (UK) Ltd, 10 Great Marlborough Street, London W1.

50

```
        C              G           C
1.  Riding on the City of New Orleans,
        Am            F              C    G7
    Illinois Central Monday morning rail,
        C              G               C
    fifteen cars and fifteen restless riders,
            F              G              C
    three conductors and twenty-five sacks of mail.
            Am                          Em
    All out on a south bound odyssey, the train pulls out of Kankakee,
        G                      D
    rolls past the houses, farms and fields.
        Am                          Em
    Passing towns that have no name and freight yards full of old black men
                F            G7          C
    and the grave-yards of rusted automobiles.
                    F            G        C
Ref.:  Singing: Good morning America, how are you?
        Am              F            C    G7
    Don't you know me, I'm your native son.
            C              G             C
    I'm the train they call the City of New Orleans
                F              G7                    C
    and I'll be gone five hundred miles, when the day is done.
        C              G           C
2.  Dealin' cards to the old man in the club car,
        Am            F              C    G7
    Penny-a-point and no one's keepin' score,
        C              G               C
    pass the paper bag that holds the bottle,
            F              G              C
    you can feel the wheels grumblin' 'neath the floor.
            Am                          Em
    The sons of Pullman porters and the sons of engineers
        G                      D
    ride their fathers' magic carpets made of steam.
            Am                          Em
    And mothers with their babies asleep are rocking in a gentle beat,
            F            G7          C
    the rhythm of the rail is all they dream.  *Refrain*
        C              G           C
3.  Nighttime on the „City of New Orleans",
        Am            F              C    G7
    changing cars in Memphis, Tennessee,
        C              G               C
    halfway home and we'll be there by morning,
                F              G              C
    through the Mississippi darkness rolling' to the sea .
            Am                          Em
    But all the towns and people seem to fade into a bad dream,
        G                      D
    the steel rail hasn't heard the news.
            Am                          Em
    The conductor sings his songs again, its passengers will please refrain,
            F            G7          C
    this train's got the disappearin' railroad blues.  *Refrain*
```

51

COULD YOU BE LOVED

♩ 92 | Reggae

Could you be loved and be loved?

Don't let them fool you or e-ven try to school you,

oh, no. We've got a mind of our own. So, go to

hell if what you're think-in' is-n't right. Love would nev-er

leave us a-lone, in the dark-ness there must come out the light.

Could you be loved and be loved?

The road of life is rock-y and you may stum-ble too. So

while you point your fin-gers, some-one else is judg-in' you. Love

— your bro-ther man. Could you be, could you be loved?

Could you be, could you be, could you be loved?

Could you be, could you be loved?

D.S. al

52

Stay a-live, oh. Could you be loved__ and be loved?

You ain't gon-na miss your wa - ter un -

til your well runs dry.__ No mat - ter how you treat him, the man will

nev-er be sat-is-fied. Could you be, could you be, could you be loved?

Could you be, could you be loved? Say some-thin', say some-thin'.

Words & Music by Bob Marley

G   **Em C**   **G**   **Em C**   **G**
Could you be loved and be loved? Could you be loved and be loved?

Em   **Am Em**   **Am**
1. Don't let them fool you   or even try to school you,   oh, no.
Em   **C**   **Bm**   **Am**
We've got a mind of our own, so go to hell, if what you're thinkin' isn't right.
Em   **C**   **Bm**   **D**
Love would never leave us alone, in the darkness there must come out the light.
G   **Em C**   **G**   **Em C**   **G**
Could you be loved and be loved? Could you be loved and be loved?
Em
The road of life is rocky and you might stumble, too.
So while you point your fingers, someone else ist judg'in you.
Love your brother man. Could you be, could you be loved?
Could you be, could you be, could you be loved? Could you be, could you be loved?

Em   **Am Em**   **Am**
2. Don't let them change you or even rearrange you, oh, no.
Em   **C Bm Am**
We've got a life to live, ooh, ooh, ooh.
Em   **C**   **Bm**   **D**
They say only, only, only the fittest of the fittest shall survive. Stay alive, oh.
G   **Em C**   **G**   **Em C**   **G**
Could you be loved and be loved? Could you be loved and be loved?
Em
You ain't gonna miss your water, until your well runs dry.
No matter how you treat him, the man will never be satisfied.
Could you be, could you be, could you be loved? Could you be, could you be loved?
Could you be, could you be, could you be loved? Could you be, could you be loved?
Say something, say something ... (fade out)

53

COUNTRY ROADS

♩ 144 | Country-Fox

Words & Music by Bill Danoff / John Denver / Taffy Nivert
© 1971 by CHERRY LANE MUSIC PUBL. CO. INC.
Für Deutschland, Österreich, Schweiz und ehem. Ostblockstaaten: GLOBAL MUSIKVERLAG, München

```
          G    Em              D                              C         G
1.   Almost heaven,  West Virginia, Blue Ridge Mountains, Shenandoah River.
                    Em
     Life is old there, older than the trees,
          D                          C              G
     younger than the mountains growing like a breeze.

               G            D            Em        C
Ref.: Country Roads, take me home to the place I do belong,
               G                 D           C              G
     West Virginia, mountain momma, take me home, Country Roads.

          G    Em                 D                  C              G
2.   All my mem'ries   gather 'round her, miner's lady, stranger to blue water.
                    Em
     Dark and dusty, painted on the sky,
          D                    C            G
     misty taste of moonshine - teardrop in my eye.

               G            D            Em        C
Ref.: Country Roads, take me home to the place I do belong,
               G                 D           C              G
     West Virginia, mountain momma, take me home, Country Roads.

   Em           D           G
3.   I hear her voice, in the mornin' hours she calls me,
          C        G          D
     the radio reminds me of my home far away,
             Em          F        C
     and drivin' down the road I get a feelin'
               G                 D              D7
     that I should have been home yesterday, yesterday.

               G            D            Em        C
Ref.: Country Roads, take me home to the place I do belong,
               G                 D           C              G
     West Virginia, mountain momma, take me home, Country Roads.
```

CRAZY LITTLE THING CALLED LOVE

♩ 148 | Rock 'n' Roll

This thing___ called love,___ I just ___ can't han - dle it.___ This thing___ called love, ___ I___ must a - get 'round to it,___ I ain't rea - dy.___ Cra - zy lit - tle thing called love.___ A- this thing,___ this thing, called love,___ called love,___ it___ cries ___ like a ba - by in a cra - dle all night. It swings, ooh,___ it___ jives, ___ ooh,_____ shakes all___ o - ver like a jel - ly - fish,___ I kind - a like it.___ Cra - zy lit - tle thing called love. There goes my ba - by,___ she knows how to rock and___ roll,___ she drives me cra - zy.___

56

    G   C   F   C

1.   This thing called love, I just can't handle it.

                G   C   F   C   G

    This thing called love, I must get 'round to it, I ain't ready.

     Eb   F   G

    Crazy little thing called love.

```
       G                            C                       F      C
2.   This thing called love, it cries like a baby in a cradle all night.
              G            C               F   C          G
     It swings, it jives, shakes all over like a jellyfish, I kinda like it.
        E♭          F           G
     Crazy little thing called love.

                     C              F                    C
Zw.: There goes my baby, she knows how to rock and roll,
                 E♭                      A           D
     she drives me crazy. She gives me hot and cold fever,
        B♭                            A  D7
     she leaves me in a cool, cool sweat.

              G              C         F       C
3.   I gotta be cool, relax, get hip, a-get on my tracks,
              G                         C                       F   C
     take a backseat, hitchhike. And take a long long ride on my motorbike,
              G       E♭       F           G
     until I'm ready. Crazy little thing called love.


     Instrumental Break

              G              C         F       C
4.   I gotta be cool, relax, get hip, a-get on my tracks,
              G                         C                       F   C
     take a backseat, hitchhike. And take a long long ride on my motorbike,
                 G                        E♭        F           G
     until I'm ready  (I'm ready, Freddie). Crazy little thing called love.

     G                            C        F   C
5.   This thing called love, I just can't handle it.
              G                C      F      C         G
     This thing called love, I must get 'round to it, I ain't ready.
        E♭          F           G
     Crazy little thing called love.
        E♭          F           G
     Crazy little thing called love ... (fade out)
```

58

COCAINE

♩ 104 | Medium Rock

Words & Music by John J. Cale

        Em   D   Em
1. If you wanna hang out, you've gotta take her out; cocaine.
        Em   D   Em
    If you wanna get down, down on the ground; cocaine.

              Em   D   C B Em D Em D
    She don't lie, she don't lie, she don't lie; cocaine.

              Em   D   Em
2. If you got bad news, you wanna kick them blues; cocaine.
              Em   D   Em
    When your day is done, and ya wanna run; cocaine.   She don't lie ...

3. *Instrumental*

              Em   D   Em
4. If your thing is gone and ya wanna ride on; cocaine.
              Em   D   Em
    Don't forget this fact can't get back; cocaine.   She don't lie ...

CROCODILE ROCK

♩ 144 | Rock

I re-mem - ber when Rock was young,___ me and Su-sie had so much fun,___ hold-ing hands___ and ski-min' stones, had an old___ gold Chev - y and a place of my own. But the big-gest kick I e - ver got___ was do-in' a thing called the Cro-co-dile Rock.___ While the oth - er kids were Rock-in' round the Clock, we were hop-pin' and bop - pin' to the Cro-co-dile Rock, well Cro-co-dile Rock-in' is some - thing shock - in' when your feet just can't keep still.___ I ne-ver knew me a bet-ter time___ and I guess I nev - er___ will. Oh,___ Law-dy ma-ma those Fri - day nights when Su - sie wore her dres-ses tight___ and the Cro-co-dile___ Rock-in' was___ out of sight.___ La___ la la la la la,___ la la la la la,___

la la la la la.   But the years

La___ la la la la la,___ la la la la la,___ la la la la la.   repeat and
fade out

      D   **F#m**

1.   I remember when Rock was young me and Susie had so much fun,
        G
     holding hands and skimin' stones,
       A
     had an old gold Chevy and a place of my own.
       D
     But the biggest kick I ever got
         F#m
     was doin' a thing called the Crocodile Rock.
          G
     While the other kids were Rockin' round the Clock,
         A
     we were hoppin' and boppin' to the Crocodile Rock, well

  Hm   **A Hm A Hm A   Hm A**
Ref.: Crocodile Rockin' is something shockin'
       Hm   **E7**
     when your feet just can't keep still.
  A7   **D**
     I never knew me a better time and I guess I never will.
     H   **E7**
     Oh, Lawdy mama those Friday nights, when Susie wore her dresses tight
       A7   **G**
     and   the Crocodile Rockin' was out of sight.
     D   **Hm**   **G**   **A**
     La la la la la la, la la la la la, la la la la la.

                 D

2.   But the years went by and rock just died.
     F#m
     Susie went and left me for some foreign guy.
          G
     Long nights cryin' by the record machine,
     A
     dreamin' of my Chevy and my old blue jeans
          D   **F#m**
     But they'll never kill the thrills we've got burning up the crocodile rock,
         G
     learning fast 'till the weeks went past,
      A
     we really thought the crocodile rock would last.

  Hm   **A Hm A Hm A   Hm A**
Ref.: Crocodile Rockin' is something shockin' ... *(Wdh. 1. Strophe + Refrain)*

CRYIN'

♩ 70 | Slow Rock

There was a time___ when I was so bro-ken-heart-ed.

Love was-n't much___ of a friend of mine.___

The ta-bles have turned, yeah, 'cause me and them ways have part - ed.

That kind of love___ was the kill-in' kind.___ Lis-ten!

All I want___ is some - one I can't re - sist.

I know all I need to know by the way that I got kissed. I was

cry - in'___ when I met you. Now I'm try - in'___ to for-get you.___

Love is sweet___ mis-er-y.___ I was

cry - in'___ just to get you. Now I'm dy-in'___ 'cause I let you___

do what you do___ down on me.___ Yeah!

Now there's not e-ven breath-in' room___ between pleasure and pain.

Yeah, you cry when we're ma-kin' love.____ Must be one and the same.

Instr. break

'Cause what you got in-side ain't where your love should stay. Yeah, our love, sweet love, ain't love till you give your heart a-way.____ Yeah,_____ I was

D.S. al ⊕-⊕

do what you, do what you do down to me, ba-by, ba-by, ba-by, ba-by, ba-by, ba-by.

Instr. break

I was

D.S. al ⊕-⊕⊕

do what you do_____ down to, down to, down to, down to, down to.

I was cry-in' when I met you. Now I'm try-in' to for-get you.____

Your___ love is sweet.____ I was

cry-in' when I met you. Now I'm dy-in'___ 'cause I let you.___ (fade)

Words & Music by Steve Tyler, Joe Perry & Taylor Rhodes

© 1993 Swagsongs Music Incorporated & T. Rhodes Songs/MCA Music Incorporated, USA
BMG Music Publishing Ltd, 69/79 Fulham High Street, London SW6 (66,66%)/Universal/MCA Music Limited,
77 Fulham Palace Road, London SW6 (33,33%)

```
    A                  E   F#m                  C#m
1.  There was a time      when I was so broken-hearted .
    D                 A       E
    Love wasn't much of a friend of mine.
    A                      E               F#m                    C#m
    The tables have turned, yeah,    'cause me and them ways have parted.
    D                  A           E
    That kind of love was the killin' kind. Listen!
    G        D           G              D
    All I want is someone I can't resist.
    C              G                        E
    I know all I  need to know by the way that I got kissed.

              A                E                     F#m          D
Ref.:  I was cryin', when I met you. Now I'm tryin' to forget you.
    A           E        D
    Love is sweet misery.
              A                E                C#m           D
    I was cryin' just to get you. Now I'm dyin' cause I let you
    A               E              D
    do what you do down on me. Yeah!

    G                                   B♭ C FG                                 B♭ C F
Zw.: Now there's not even breathin' room        between pleasure and pain.
    G                                   B♭ C F G                           B♭
    Yeah, you cry when we're makin' love.        Must be one and the same.

   A                  E  F#m           C#m
2.  It's down on me, yeah, I got to tell you one thing.
    D                      A         E
    It's been on my mind, girl, I gotta say.
    A                       E      F#m        C#m
    We're partners in crime. You got that certain something.
    D                         A            E
    What you give to me takes my breath away.
               G                    D         G               D
    Now, the word out on the street is the devil's in your kiss.
    C                   G                     E
    If our love goes   up in flames, it's a fire I can't resist.

              A                E                     F#m          D
Ref.:  I was cryin', when I met you. Now I'm tryin' to forget you.
    A               E        D
    Your love is sweet misery.
              A                E                C#m           D
    I was cryin' just to get you. Now I'm dyin' cause I let you
    A               E       D
    do what you do to me. Yeah!
```

Instrumental break

```
               E♭               B♭             E♭                          B♭
Zw.: 'Cause what you got inside ain't where your love should stay.
          A♭                   E♭                E
    Yeah,  our love, sweet love,   ain't love till you give your heart away. Yeah
```

     A   E   C#m   D
Ref.: I was cryin', when I met you. Now I'm tryin' to forget you.
 A   E   D
 Your love is sweet misery.
     A   E   F#m   D
 I was cryin' just to get you. Now I'm dyin' cause I let you
 A   E   D
 do what you, do what you do down to me, baby, baby, baby, baby, baby, baby.

Instrumental break

     A   E   C#m   D
Ref.: I was cryin', when I met you. Now I'm tryin' to forget you.
 A   E   D
 Your love is sweet misery. Yeah!
     A   E   F#m   D
 I was cryin', when I met you. Now I'm dyin' cause I let you
 A   E   D
 do what you do down to,   down to, down to, down to, down to.

     A   E   C#m   D
Ref.: I was cryin', when I met you. Now I'm tryin' to forget you.
 A   E D
 Your love is sweet.
     A   E   C#m   D
 I was cryin', when I met you. Now I'm dyin' cause I let you. *(fade)*

DANCING QUEEN

♩ 104 | Moderato-Beat

You can dance, you can jive,_____

ha - ving the time of your life._____ Ooh_____ see that__ girl,__

watch that__ scene dig-gin' the danc-ing__ queen.

Fri - day night__ and the lights are low,___ look-ing out for a place to go__

___ where they play__ the right mu - sic get-ting in__ the swing you come to

look for a king.__ An - y - bo - dy could be that guy,__

night is young and the mu - sic's high. With a bit__ of rock mu-sic

ev' - ry thing is fine,__ you're in the mood for a dance and when you

get the__ chance you are the danc-ing queen young and sweet__ on - ly

se - ven - teen._____ Danc-ing__ queen__ feel the__ beat__ from the

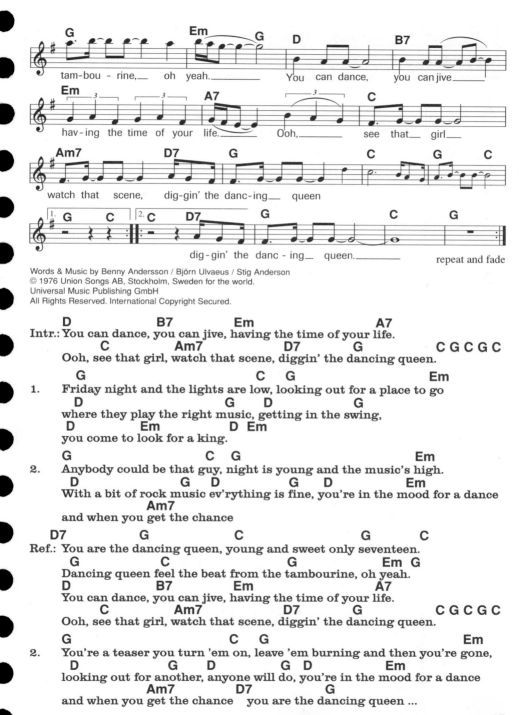

```
              D                 B7             Em                       A7
Intr.: You can dance, you can jive, having the time of your life.
                    C              Am7              D7              G          C G C G C
              Ooh, see that girl, watch that scene, diggin' the dancing queen.
              G                              C     G                      Em
1.      Friday night and the lights are low, looking out for a place to go
              D                      G     D                   G
        where they play the right music, getting in the swing,
              D        Em            D Em
        you come to look for a king.
              G                            C    G                       Em
2.      Anybody could be that guy, night is young and the music's high.
              D                G    D               G     D              Em
        With a bit of rock music ev'rything is fine, you're in the mood for a dance
                        Am7
        and when you get the chance
        D7              G                C                     G          C
Ref.: You are the dancing queen, young and sweet only seventeen.
              G                 C                     G              Em G
        Dancing queen feel the beat from the tambourine, oh yeah.
              D                 B7             Em                       A7
        You can dance, you can jive, having the time of your life.
                    C              Am7              D7              G          C G C G C
        Ooh, see that girl, watch that scene, diggin' the dancing queen.
              G                              C     G                      Em
2.      You're a teaser you turn 'em on, leave 'em burning and then you're gone,
              D                      G     D               G     D        Em
        looking out for another, anyone will do, you're in the mood for a dance
                        Am7             D7              G
        and when you get the chance   you are the dancing queen ...
```

DON'T THINK TWICE, IT'S ALL RIGHT

♩ 92 | Ballade

Words & Music by Bob Dylan

1.
    G   D   Em   C   G
It ain't no use to sit and wonder why, babe. If you don't know by now.
D7 G   D   Em   A7   D
An' it ain't no use to sit and wonder why, babe. It don't matter anyhow.
D7   G   G7
When the rooster crows at the break of dawn,
C   A7   G   D   Em C
look out your window and I'll be gone. You're the reason I'm trav'lin' on.
G   D7   G
Don't think twice, it's all right.

2.
    G   D   Em   C   G
It ain't no use in turnin' on your light, babe, the light I never knowed.
D7 G   D   Em   A7   D
It ain't no use in turnin' on your light, babe, I'm on the dark side of the road.
D7   G   G7
Still I wish there was something you could do or say
C   A7   G   D   Em   C
to try to change my mind and stay. We never did too much talkin' anyway,
G   D7   G
so don't think twice, it's all right.

```
        G              D           Em      C                           G
3.   It ain't no use in callin' out my name, gal,  like you never did before.
   D7   G          D            Em       A7                          D
     It ain't no use in callin' out my name, gal,   I can't hear you anymore.
   D7        G                       G7
     I'm a-thinkin' and a-wond'rin' all the   way down the road.
   C                          A7
     I once loved a woman, a child, I'm told.
   G              D            Em        C
     I'd give her my heart, but she wanted my soul.
   G              D7         G
     But don't think twice, it's all right.

        G              D           Em      C                           G
4.   I'm walkin' down that long lonesome road, babe, where I'm bound, I can't tell.
   D7   G          D            Em       A7                          D
     But good-bye's too good a word, babe,   so I'll just say fare-thee-well.
   D7        G                G7
     I ain't sayin' you treated   me unkind,
   C                          A7
     you could have done better, but I don't mind.
   G              D            Em    C
     You just kind-a wasted my precious time.
   G              D7         G
     But don't think twice, it's all right.
```

DOWN UNDER

%
D   A   Bm   G   A

"I come from a land down un-der.____

D   A   Bm   G   A

Where beer does flow_   and men chun-der.

D   A   Bm   G   A

Can't you hear, can't you hear the thun-der?____   You

D   A   1. Bm   G   A   2. Bm   G   A %

bet-ter run,__ you bet-ter take_ cov-er."____   —   D.S. and fade out

Words & Music by Colin Hay / Ron Strykert
© 1982 EMI Songs Australia Pty Ltd. EMI Songs Ltd., London WC2H 0QY
Reproduced by permission of IMP Ltd. All Rights Reserved

Bm   A   Bm G A
1.   Traveling in a fried-out combie.
Bm   A   Bm   G A
    On a hippie trail, head full of zombie.
Bm   A   Bm   G A
    I met a strange lady.   She made me nervous.
Bm   A   Bm   G   A
    She took me in and gave me breakfast. And she said:

D   A   Bm G A
Ref.: "Do you come from a land down under?
    D   A   Bm G A
    Where women glow and men plunder.
    D   A   Bm G A
    Can't you hear, can't you hear the thunder?
          D   A   Bm   G A Bm A Bm G A Bm A Bm G A
    You better run, you better take cover."

Bm   A   Bm G   A
2.   Buying bread from a man in Brussels.   He was
Bm   A   Bm   G A
    six foot four and full of muscels.
Bm   A   Bm   G A
    I said: "Do you speak my language?"
    Bm   A   Bm   G   A
    He just smiled and gave me a vegemite sandwich. He said: *Refrain*

Bm   A   Bm G A
3.   Lying in a den in Bombay.
Bm   A   Bm   G A
    With a slack jaw and not much to say.
Bm   A   Bm   G A
    I said to the man: "Are you trying to tempt me
Bm   A   Bm   G   A   D
    because I come from the land of plenty?" And he said: "Oh! *Refrain*

71

DOWNTOWN

Words & Music by Tony Hatch
© 1964 ATV Music
Sony/ATV Music Publishing (UK) Ltd., 10 Great Marlborough Street, London W1
All Rights Reserved. International Copyright Secured.

```
         G            Bm                C            D7           G      Bm
1.   When you're alone and life is making you lonely, you can always go
     C       D
     Downtown.
         G            Bm                C            D7              G      Bm
     When you've got worries, all the noise and the hurry seems to help I know,
     C       D
     Downtown.
         G                      Em
     Just listen to the music of the traffic in the city.
      G                          Em
     Linger on the sidewalk, where the neon signs are pretty.
      Bm
     How can you lose?
     C
     The lights are much brighter there,
                 A7
     you can forget all your troubles, forget all your cares.

              G    Bm   C              D              G      Bm
Ref.: So go Downtown, things will be great, when you're Downtown
         C          D          G    Bm  C          D7          G
     No finer place, for sure, Downtown. Ev'rything's waiting for you.

         G            Bm                C            D7                 G      Bm
2.   Don't hang around and let your problems surround you, there are movie shows
       C    D
     Downtown.
         G            Bm              C      D7           G      Bm
     Maybe you know some little places to go to where they never close,
     C       D
     Downtown.
         G                      Em
     Just listen to the rhythm of the gentle Bossanova,
      G                          Em
     you'll be dancing with him 'till before the night is over,
      Bm
     happy again.
     C
     The lights are much brighter there,
                 A7
     you can forget all your troubles, forget all your cares.

              G    Bm   C              D              G      Bm
Ref.: So go Downtown, where are the lights so bright, Downtown,
         C          D          G    Bm  C          D7          G
     waiting for you tonight, Downtown, you're gonna be all right now.
```

EVE OF DESTRUCTION

♩ | 118 | Rock

Words & Music by P.F. Sloan
© 1965 MCA Music (a division of MCA Incorporated, USA)
Universal/MCA Music Limited, 77 Fulham Palace Road, London W6
All Rights Reserved. International Copyright Secured.

74

```
     D                  G            A7   D              G          A7
1.   The eastern world  it is explodin' violence flarin', bullets loadin',
         D             G              A7
     you're old enough to kill  but not for votin',
             D                 G                    A7
     you don't believe in war, what's that gun you're totin',
         D                      G           A7
     and even the Jordan river has   bodies floatin'.
                 D       G      A7      D            Bm
Ref.: But you   tell me over and over and over again my friend,
          G                  A7              D
     ah, you don't believe we're on the eve of destruction.

     D                       G                A7
2.   Don't you understand,   what I'm trying to say?
     D                    G              A7
     Can't you see the fear   that I'm feeling today
             D              G             A7
     If the button is pushed, there's no runnin' away,
          D                   G            A7
     there'll be no one to save with the world in a grave,
               D         G        A7                A7
     take a look around you, boy,   it's bound to scare you, boy. Refrain

             D          G          A7
3.   Yeah, my blood's so mad, feels like coagulatin',
     D            G           A7
     I'm sittin' here, just contemplatin',
         D                  G               A7
     I can't twist the truth, it knows no regulation,
           D                  G          A7
     handful of senators don't pass legislation,
             D                G         A7
     and marches alone can't bring integration,
              D           G        A7
     when human respect is disintegratin',
               D             G          A7
     this whole crazy world is just too frustratin'. Refrain

     D                    G                A7
3.   Think of all the hate there is in Red China!
            D              G           A7
     Then take a look around to Selma, Alabama!
           D                G             A7
     Ah, you may leave her, for four days in space,
          D              G            A7
     but when you return, it's the same old place,
           D                 G             A7
     the poundin' of the drums, the pride an' disgrace,
              D             G          A7
     you can bury your dead, but don't leave a trace,
               D              G                A7
     it's your next-door-neighbour, but don't forget to say grace and Refrain

      D        G        A7      F#m           Bm
Ref.: tell me over and over and over and over again, my friend,
         G                   A7              D
     ||: you don't believe we're on the eve of destruction. :||
```

75

EVERY BREATH YOU TAKE

♩ 126 | Beat

Ev'-ry breath you take, ev'-ry move you make,

ev'-ry bond you break, ev'-ry step you take, I'll be watch-ing you.

Oh can't you__ see you be-long to me.

How my poor heart aches__ with ev'-ry step__ you take.

Since you've gone I've been lost__ with-out_____ a trace, I dream at night I can on-

ly see__ your face. I look a-round but it's you I can't re-place,

I feel so cold and I long for your em-brace. I keep call-ing ba-

by, ba-by, please._____

D.S., dann
3. Strophe

Words & Music by Sting
© 1983 G.M. Summer
EMI Music Publishing Limited/Magnetic Publishing Limited.

E   C#m
1.   Ev'ry breath you take, ev'ry move you make,
               A   B   C#m
    ev'ry bond you break, ev'ry step you take, I'll be watching you.

        E   C#m

2.   Ev'ry single day, ev'ry word you say,

                     A   B   E

      ev'ry game you play, ev'ry night you stay, I'll be watching you.

       E   A A7   E

Zw.: Oh, can't you see   you belong to me.

                      F#7   B

      How my heart aches with ev'ry step you take.

       E   C#m

3.   Ev'ry move you make, ev'ry vow you break,

                     A   B   E

      ev'ry smile you fake, ev'ry claim you stake, I'll be watching you.

       C

Zw.: Since you've gone I've been lost without a trace,

       D

      I dream at night I can only see your face.

       C

      I look around, but it's you I can't replace,

       D

      I feel so cold and I long for your embrace.

       C   E   C#m A B C#m

      I keep calling baby, baby, please.

       E   A

Zw.: Oh, can't you see ...

       E

3.   Ev'ry move you make ...

EVERY ROSE HAS ITS THORN

♩ 70 | Slow Beat

We both lie si-lent-ly still in the dead of the night. Al-though we

both lie close to-geth - er,__ we feel miles a-part__ in-side.__ Was it

something I said or something I did? Did my words not come out right? Though I

tried not to hurt you,__ though I tried. But I guess that's why__ they say

ev' - ry rose has its thorn, just like ev' - ry night has its

dawn._____ Just like ev' - ry cow-boy__ sings his sad, sad song,

ev' - ry rose has its thorn. *(gespr.:) yeah it does*

I thorn.

Though it's been a while now, I can still feel so much pain.__

Like the knife that cuts you, the wound heals, but the scar, that scar re - mains.

78

11

(Instr. Improvisation)

I know I could have saved our love that night__ if I'd known what to say.__ In-stead of mak - ing love__ we both made our sep'-rate ways. Now I hear you've found some - bod - y new and that I nev-er meant that much to you. To hear that tears me up in-side__ and to see you cuts me like a knife. I guess ev' - ry rose has its thorn, just like ev' - ry night has its dawn.__ Just like ev' - ry cow-boy__ sings his sad, sad song, ev' - ry rose has its thorn.

Words & Music by Bret Michael Sychak/Richard Ream/Bruce Johannesson/Robert Kuykendall
© by Cyanide Publishing / Zomba Songs Inc.
Für D/A/CH, Rumänien, Bulgarien, Albanien, GUS und ehem. Jugoslawien: Musik-Edition Disoton GmbH (BMG UFA), München

```
        G                                   C
1.   We both lie silently still in the dead of the night.
             G                                    C
     Although we both lie close together, we feel miles apart inside.
            G                     C                      G              C
     Was it something I said or something I did? Did my words not come out right?
             D                            C
     Though I tried not to hurt you, though I tried. But I guess that's why they say,

          G                C             G                C
Ref.: Ev'ry rose has its thorn, just like ev'ry night has its dawn.
               G      D               C      G                          C
      Just like ev'ry cowboy sings his sad, sad song, ev'ry rose has its thorn.

          G                              C
2.   I listen to our favorite song playing on the radio,
                G                                   C
     hear the D. J. say love's a game of easy come and   easy go.
            G            C        G           C
     But I wonder does he know, has he ever felt like this?
             D                               C
     And I know that you'd be here right now, if I   could've let you know somehow.
     I guess

          G                C             G                C
Ref.: Ev'ry rose has its thorn, just like ev'ry night has its dawn.
               G      D               C      G                          C
      Just like ev'ry cowboy sings his sad, sad song, ev'ry rose has its thorn.

     Em                    D            C              G
Zw.:  Though it's been a while, now I can still feel so much pain.
     Em                    D                  C                        G
      Like the knife that cuts you, the wound heals,  but the scar, that scar remains.

     Instrumental Improvisation

     G                                         C
3.   I know I could have saved our love that night, if I'd   known what to say.
     G                       C
     Instead of making love we both   made our separate ways.
            G                  C            G                    C
     Now I hear you've found somebody new and that I never meant that much to you.
             D                            C
     To hear that tears me up inside and to see you cuts me like a knife. I guess

          G                C             G                C
Ref.: Ev'ry rose has its thorn, just like ev'ry night has its dawn.
               G      D               C      G                  C  D G
      Just like ev'ry cowboy sings his sad, sad song, ev'ry rose has its thorn.
```

EL CONDOR PASA

♩ 76 | Slow-Beat

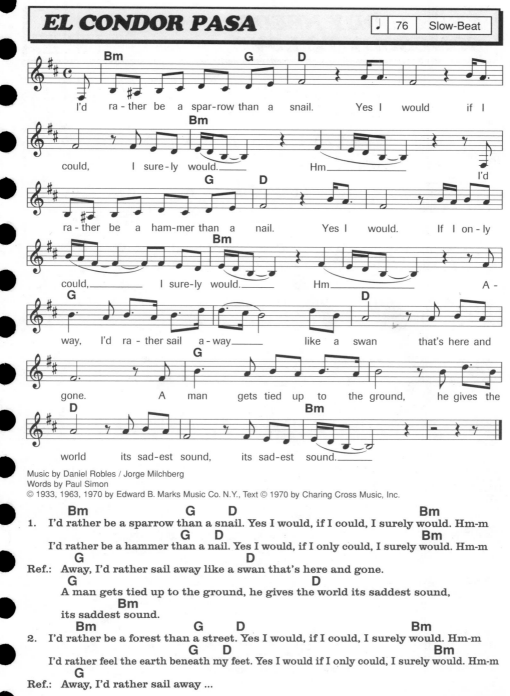

Music by Daniel Robles / Jorge Milchberg
Words by Paul Simon

    Bm   **G**   **D**   **Bm**
1. I'd rather be a sparrow than a snail. Yes I would, if I could, I surely would. Hm-m
                      G   **D**   **Bm**
     I'd rather be a hammer than a nail. Yes I would, if I only could, I surely would. Hm-m
         G   **D**
Ref.: Away, I'd rather sail away like a swan that's here and gone.
         G   **D**
     A man gets tied up to the ground, he gives the world its saddest sound,
             Bm
     its saddest sound.
         Bm   **G**   **D**   **Bm**
2. I'd rather be a forest than a street. Yes I would, if I could, I surely would. Hm-m
                      G   **D**   **Bm**
     I'd rather feel the earth beneath my feet. Yes I would if I only could, I surely would. Hm-m
         G
Ref.: Away, I'd rather sail away ...

EVERYBODY NEEDS SOMEBODY TO LOVE

♩ 188 | Jive

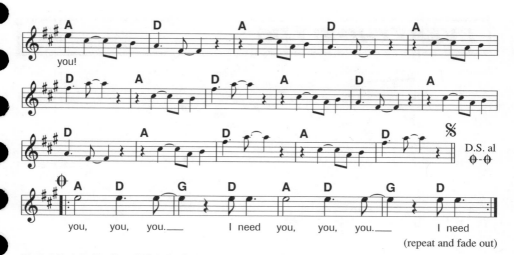

you!

you, you, you.___ I need you, you, you.___ I need

(repeat and fade out)

Words & Music by Bert Russell / Solomon Burke / Jerry Wexler
© 1965 by KEETCH, CAESAR AND DINO MUSIC INC.
Subverlag für D/A/CH: ROBERT MELLIN MUSIKVERLAG KG

A DGDA D GDA DGDA D GD A DG
Everybody needs somebody. Everybody needs somebody to love.
D A DG D A DG D A DG
Someone to love, sweetheart to miss, sugar to kiss.
D A D G D A D G D A D G
I need you, you, you. I need you, you, you. I need you, you, you.
D A DG D A DGD
In the morning when my soul's on fire.

F#m D7
Sometimes I feel, I feel a little sad inside.
F#m E7
When my baby mistreats me, I never, never, never got nothin' to hide!
A DADADADADADADAD
I need you!

F#m D7
Sometimes I feel, I feel a little sad inside.
F#m E7
When my baby mistreats me, I never, never, never got nothin' to hide!
A D G D A D G D A D G
I need you, you, you. I need you, you, you. I need you, you, you ... *(fade out)*

EVERYTHING I DO

84

not worth try - in' for,   I can't help___ it, there's noth-ing I want

more.   Yeah,___ I would fight___ for you,___ I'd lie___ for you,

walk the wire for you,___ yeah, I'd die for_ you.___

     You know, it's   true,   ev'-ry-thing I   do,

oh,___   I do it for_ you.___

Words by Bryan Adams & Robert John 'Mutt' Lange - Music by Michael Kamen
© 1991 by Out of Pocket Productions Ltd., administered by Zomba Music Publishers Ltd., 165-167 High Road,
London NW10 (18,75%) / Miracle Creek Music & Zachary Creek Music, administered by Universal/MCA Music Ltd.,
77 Fulham Road, London W6 (62,5%) / Rondor Music Ltd., London W6 8JA (18,75%)
Reproduced by permission of IMP Ltd. All Rights Reserved. International Copyright Secured.

          F   Bb   C

1.   **Look into my eyes, you will see there's what you mean to me.**
                 F   Bb
      Search your heart, search your soul, and when you find me there
           F   C   Gm   F   Gm
      you'll search no more. Don't tell me it's not worth tryin' for,
                                  F   Gm
      you can't tell me it's not worth dyin' for.
                     F   C   F
      You know it's true, ev'rything I do, I do it for you.

          F   Bb   C

2.   **Look into your heart, you will find there's nothing there to hide.**
                 F   Bb
      Take me as I am, take my life, I would give it all,
           F   C   Gm   F   Gm
      I would sacrifice. Don't tell me it's not worth fightin' for,
                                F   Gm
      I can't help it, there's nothing I want more.
                     F   C   F
      You know it's true, ev'rything I do, I do it for you.
                     Eb   Ab   Eb   Bb
      There's no love like your love and no other could give more love,
                F   C   G   C
      there's nowhere unless you're there all the time, all the way, yeah.
                 Gm   F   C   Gm
      Oh, you can't tell me it's not worth tryin' for, I can't help it,
                              C   F
      there's nothing I want more. Yeah, I would figth for you,
           C   Bb   Bbm
      I'd lie for you, walk the wire for you, yeah, I'd die for you.
                     F   C   Bb   F
      You know it's true, ev'rything I do, oh, I do it for you.

85

FAR, FAR AWAY

♩ 112 | Medium Rock

I've seen the yel-low lights go down the Mis-sis-sip - pi, I've seen the bridg-es of the world, and they're for real; I've had a red light of the wrist with-out me e - ven get-tin' kissed; it still seems so un-real. I've seen the (best) And I'm far, far a-way with my head up in the clouds. And I'm far, far a-way with my feet down in the crowds. Let - tin' loose a-round the world, but the call of home is loud, still as loud.

2x D.S., 2.x al

I've seen the And I'm far, far a-way with my head up in the clouds. And I'm far, far a-way with my feet down in the crowds. Let - tin'

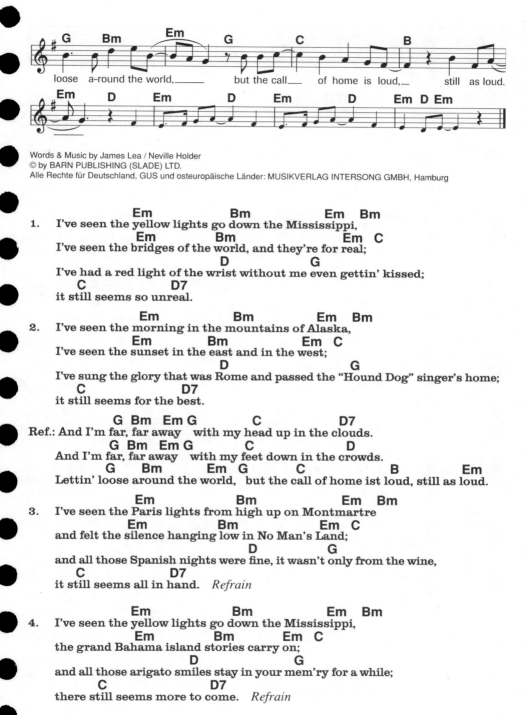

loose a-round the world,___ but the call___ of home is loud,___ still as loud.

Words & Music by James Lea / Neville Holder
© by BARN PUBLISHING (SLADE) LTD.
Alle Rechte für Deutschland, GUS und osteuropäische Länder: MUSIKVERLAG INTERSONG GMBH, Hamburg

1.   **Em**   **Bm**   **Em** **Bm**
I've seen the yellow lights go down the Mississippi,
            Em   **Bm**   **Em** **C**
I've seen the bridges of the world, and they're for real;
              D   **G**
I've had a red light of the wrist without me even gettin' kissed;
C   **D7**
it still seems so unreal.

2.   **Em**   **Bm**   **Em** **Bm**
I've seen the morning in the mountains of Alaska,
            Em   **Bm**   **Em** **C**
I've seen the sunset in the east and in the west;
              D   **G**
I've sung the glory that was Rome and passed the "Hound Dog" singer's home;
C   **D7**
it still seems for the best.

          G **Bm** **Em** **G**   **C**   **D7**
Ref.: And I'm far, far away   with my head up in the clouds.
          G **Bm** **Em** **G**   **C**   **D**
And I'm far, far away   with my feet down in the crowds.
          G **Bm**   **Em** **G**   **C**   **B**   **Em**
Lettin' loose around the world, but the call of home ist loud, still as loud.

3.   **Em**   **Bm**   **Em** **Bm**
I've seen the Paris lights from high up on Montmartre
            Em   **Bm**   **Em** **C**
and felt the silence hanging low in No Man's Land;
              D   **G**
and all those Spanish nights were fine, it wasn't only from the wine,
C   **D7**
it still seems all in hand. *Refrain*

4.   **Em**   **Bm**   **Em** **Bm**
I've seen the yellow lights go down the Mississippi,
            Em   **Bm**   **Em** **C**
the grand Bahama island stories carry on;
              D   **G**
and all those arigato smiles stay in your mem'ry for a while;
C   **D7**
there still seems more to come. *Refrain*

FATHER AND SON

♩ 66 | Slow-Beat

It's not time to make a change, just re-lax take it ea - sy, you're still young, that's your fault, there's so much you have to know.__ Find a girl,__ set-tle down, if you want you can ma - ry, look at me,__

1. __ I am old but I'm hap-py. I was still be here to-mor-row but your dreams may not. How can I try__ to ex-plain? When I do__ he turns a-way a-gain. It's al - ways__ been the same, same old sto - ry. From the mo-ment__ I could talk I was or-dered to lis - ten now there's a way and I know that I have to go a - way.__ I know, I have to go.

D.C. (mit Wdh.) al ⊕-⊕

Words & Music by Cat Stevens

```
                    G              Bm            C        Am7
Father: It's not time to make a change, just relax, take it easy,
                    G                Em             Am              D
        you're still young, that's your fault, there's so much you have to know.
                    G       Bm          C          Am7
        Find a girl, settle down, if you want you can mary
                    G      Em        Am    D
        look at me, I am old, but I'm happy.

                    G              Bm          C              Am7
        I was once like your are now and I know that it's not easy
                    G            Em            Am         D
        to be calm, when you found something going on.
                    G              Bm            C                  Am7
        But take your time, think a lot, think of ev'rything you've got
                    G                Em                 D         G   G C
        for you will still be here tomorrow, but your dreams may not.

                    G            Bm          C          Am7
Son:    How can I try to explain? When I do he turns away again.
                    G              Em          Am  D
        It's always been the same, same old story.
                    G              Bm        C           Am7
        From the moment I could talk I was ordered to listen,
                    G        Em          D      G
        now there's a way and I know that I have to go away.
                    D      C      G
        I know, I have to go.

                    G              Bm            C        Am7
Father: It's not time to make a change, just sit down, take it slowly,
                    G                Em             Am              D
        you're still young, that's your fault, there's so much you have to go through.
                    G       Bm          C          Am7
        Find a girl, settle down, if you want you can mary
                    G      Em        Am    D
        look at me, I am old, but I'm happy.

                    G              Bm          C              Am7
Son:    All the times that I've cried, keeping all the things I knew inside,
                    G            Em          Am    D
        it's hard, but it's harder to ignore it.
                    G              Bm        C            Am7
        If they were right, I'd agree, but it's them they know not me,
                    G        Em          D      G
        now there's a way and I know that I have to go away.
                    D      C      G
        I know, I have to go.
```

FOREVER YOUNG

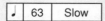

Let's dance in style. let's dance for a while. Heav-en can wait. We're on - ly watching the skies,

hoping for the best but ex-pect-ing the worst. Are you goin' to drop the bomb or not?

Let us die young or let us live for-ev – er. We don't have the pow - er but we nev-er say nev-

er sti-ting in a sand - pit. Life is a short trip. The mu-sic's for the sad__ men.

Can you i-ma - gine when this race is won? Turn our gol-den fa - ces in-to the sun.

Prais-ing our lead - ers, we're get-ting in tune. The mu-sic's played by the mad men.__

For-ev – er young, I want to be__ for-ev – er young.

Do you real - ly want to live for-ev - er, for-ev - er, and ev - er.

For-ev – er young, I want to be__ for-ev – er young.

Do you real - ly want to live for-ev - er, for-ev - er

young.   for-ev – er,   and ev – er.   For-ev – er young,   I want to be

for-ev – er young.   Do you real-ly want to live for-ev – er___

___   young.

Music by Marian Gold / Bernhard Lloyd / Frank Mertens
Words by Marian Gold
© 1984 by Rolf Budde Musikverlag GmbH, Berlin

```
         C                 G                        Am
1.    Let's dance in style. Let's dance for a while.
                    F                              G
      Heaven can wait. We're only watching the skies,
                    Am                    F
      hoping for the best, but expecting the worst.
                          Am          G
      Are you goin' to drop the bomb or not?
      C          G                  Am
      Let us die young or let us live forever.
                    F                          G
      We don't have the power, but we never say never,
                Am                F
      sitting in a sandpit. Life is a short trip.
                       Am     G
      The music's for the sad men.
      C          G
      Can you imagine when this race is won?
Am                F
      Turn our golden faces into the sun.
      G          Am                F
      Praising our leaders, we're getting in tune.
                       Am      G
      The music's played by the   mad men.

       C        G          Am       F
Ref.: Forever young, I want to be forever young.
       G                Am      F      G
      Do you really want to live forever,  forever,  and ever.
       C        G          Am       F
      Forever young, I want to be forever young.
       G                Am      F G       C    G
      Do you really want to live forever,    forever young.
```

91

```
        C              G                    Am
2.    Some are like water, some are like heat.
                    F                        G
      Some are a melody and some are the beat.
              Am                    F
      Sooner or later, they all will be gone.
                          Am      G
      Why don't they stay young?
      C              G                Am
      It's hard to get old without a cause.
                      F                      G
      I don't want to perish like a fading horse.
              Am                          F
      So many adventures couldn't happen today.
                          Am        G
      So many songs we forgot to play.
      C          G
      So many dreams swinging out of the blue.
      F                  G
      We'll let them come true.


        C          G              Am          F
Ref.: Forever young, I want to be forever young.
      G                    Am        F      G
      Do you really want to live forever,  forever,  and ever.
      C          G              Am          F
      Forever young, I want to be forever young.
      G                    Am        F      G
      Do you really want to live forever,  forever,  and ever.
      C          G              Am          F
      Forever young, I want to be forever young.
      G                    Am        F G   C      G Am F G Am F Am
      Do you really want to live forever    young.  (repeat and fade out)
```

FIVE HUNDRED MILES

♩ 126 | Medium-Beat

If you miss the train I'm on, you will know that I am gone, you can hear the whis-tle blow ohne hun - dred miles,_____ one hun - dred miles, one hun - dred miles, one hun - dred miles, one hun - dred miles, you can hear the whis - tle blow ohne hun - dred miles._____

Words & Music by Hedy West
© 1962 by Friendship Music Corp., New York
© 1962 für Deutschland, Österreich und die Schweiz by
Music-Edition Europaton / Peter Schaeffers / Ebony Musikverlag, Berlin

1.
      G   **Em**   **Am**   **C**
If you miss the train I'm on, you will know that I am gone,
    Am   **C**   **D** **D7**
you can hear the whistle blow one hundred miles.

          G   **Em**   **Am**   **C**
Ref.: One hundred miles, one hundred miles, one hundred miles, one hundred miles,
      Am   **D7**   **G**
you can hear the whistle blow one hundred miles.

2.
          G   **Em**   **Am**   **C**
Lord, I'm one, Lord, I'm two, Lord, I'm three, Lord, I'm four,
    Am   **C**   **D** **D7**
Lord, I'm five hundred miles from my home.

          G   **Em**   **Am**   **C**
Ref.: Five hundred miles, five hundred miles, five hundred miles, five hundred miles,
      Am   **D7**   **G**
Lord, I'm five hundred miles from my home.

3.
          G   **Em**   **Am**   **C**
Not a shirt on my back, not a penny to my name,
    Am   **C**   **D** **D7**
Lord, I can't go home this way.

       G   **Em**   **Am**   **C**
Ref.: This way, this way, this way, this way,
      Am   **D7**   **G**
Lord, I can't go home this way.   If you miss the train ...

FREE FALLIN'

♩ 84 | Moderato Rock

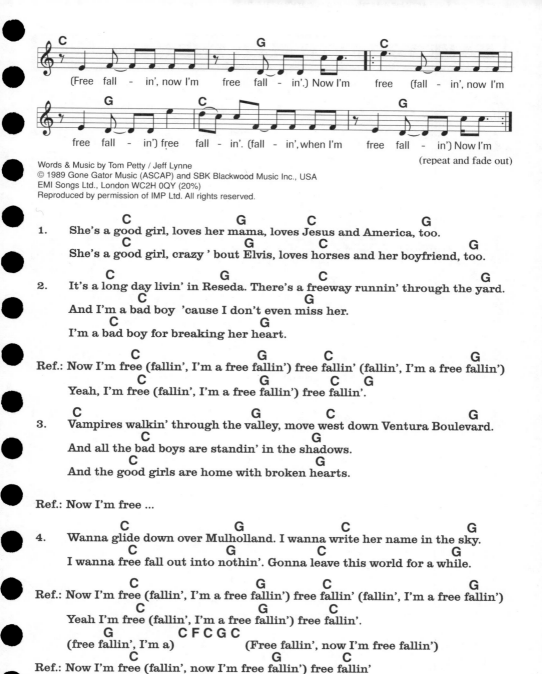

(Free fall - in', now I'm free fall - in'.) Now I'm free (fall - in', now I'm

free fall - in') free fall - in'. (fall - in', when I'm free fall - in') Now I'm

(repeat and fade out)

Words & Music by Tom Petty / Jeff Lynne
© 1989 Gone Gator Music (ASCAP) and SBK Blackwood Music Inc., USA
EMI Songs Ltd., London WC2H 0QY (20%)
Reproduced by permission of IMP Ltd. All rights reserved.

        C   G   C   G
1.   She's a good girl, loves her mama, loves Jesus and America, too.
        C   G   C   G
    She's a good girl, crazy ' bout Elvis, loves horses and her boyfriend, too.

         C   G   C   G
2.   It's a long day livin' in Reseda. There's a freeway runnin' through the yard.
        C   G
    And I'm a bad boy 'cause I don't even miss her.
        C   G
    I'm a bad boy for breaking her heart.

          C   G   C   G
Ref.: Now I'm free (fallin', I'm a free fallin') free fallin' (fallin', I'm a free fallin')
              C   G   C G
    Yeah, I'm free (fallin', I'm a free fallin') free fallin'.

        C   G   C   G
3.   Vampires walkin' through the valley, move west down Ventura Boulevard.
        C   G
    And all the bad boys are standin' in the shadows.
        C   G
    And the good girls are home with broken hearts.

Ref.: Now I'm free ...

        C   G   C   G
4.   Wanna glide down over Mulholland. I wanna write her name in the sky.
        C   G   C   G
    I wanna free fall out into nothin'. Gonna leave this world for a while.

          C   G   C   G
Ref.: Now I'm free (fallin', I'm a free fallin') free fallin' (fallin', I'm a free fallin')
            C   G   C
    Yeah I'm free (fallin', I'm a free fallin') free fallin'.
        G   C F C G C
    (free fallin', I'm a)   (Free fallin', now I'm free fallin')
        C   G   C
Ref.: Now I'm free (fallin', now I'm free fallin') free fallin'
                       G   C
    (fallin', when I'm free fallin') Now I'm free ... *(fade out)*

HAVE YOU EVER SEEN THE RAIN ♩ 118 Beat

Someone told me long a-go, there's a calm be-fore the storm, I know,
it's been com-ing for some-time. When it's o-ver, so
they say, it will rain a sun-ny day, I know, shining down like
wa-ter. I want to know, have you e-ver seen the
rain, I want to know, have you e-ver seen the rain,
com-in' down on a sun-ny day.

Words & Music by John Fogerty
© 1970 Jondora Music, USA / Prestige Music Ltd. for Europe

1.
    C   **G**

     Someone told me long ago, there's a calm before the storm, I know,

                 C
     it's been coming for sometime.

                                     G
     When it's over, so they say, it'll rain a sunny day, I know,

                    C   **C7**
     shining down like water.

           F   **G**   **C**   **G**   **Am**
Ref.: I want to know, have you ever seen the rain,
       F   **G**   **C**   **G**   **Am F**   **G**   **C**
     I want to know, have you ever seen the rain,   coming down on a sunny day.

2.
    C   **G**

     Yesterday and days before, sun is cold and rain is hard, I know,

                 C
     been that way for all my time.

                                        G
     'Till forever on it goes, thru the circle fast and slow, I know,

           C   **C7**
     I can't stop, I wonder.   *Refrain (2x)*

HEART OF GOLD

♩ | 86 | Slow-Beat

I wan-na live, I wan-na give,

I've been a min-er for a heart of gold. It's these ex-press-ions

I nev-er give that keeps me search-in' for a heart of gold,

and I'm get-tin' old. Keep me search-in' for a

heart of gold, and I'm get-tin' old. D.C.

Keep me search-in' for a heart of gold, you keep me search-in' and I'm

grow-in' old. I've been a min-er for a heart of gold.

Words & Music by Neil Young

Em   C D   G Em   C   D   G
1.   I wanna live, I wanna give,   I've been a miner for a heart of gold.
Em   C   D   G Em   G
It's these expressions I never give   that keeps me searchin' for a heart of gold,
C   Bm Am G
and I'm gettin' old.
Em   G   C   Bm Am G
Keep me searchin' for a heart of gold, and I'm gettin' old.
Em   C   D   G Em   C   D   G
2.   I've been in Hollywood, I've been in Redwood, I'd cross the ocean for a heart of gold.
Em   C   D   G Em   G
I've been in my mind, it's such a fine line   that keeps me searchin' for a heart of gold,
C   Bm Am G
and I'm gettin' old.
Em   D   Em   D   Em
Keep me searchin' for a heart of gold, you keep me searchin' and I'm growin' old.
Em   D   Em   G   C Bm Am G
Keep me searchin' for a heart of gold, I've been a miner for a heart of gold.

97

HEAVEN

♩ 70 | Slow Rock

Oh, think-in' a-bout_ all our young-er years;_ there was on - ly you_ and me;_ we were young and wild_ and free._ Now no-thing can take_ you a - way from me;_ we've been down that road be-fore,_ but that's o - ver now;_ you keep me com-in' back for more. Ba-by, you're all that I want when you're ly - in' here_ in my arms. I'm find-ing it hard to be - lieve we're in heav - en. And love is all_ that we need, and I found it there in your heart. It is - n't too hard to see_ we're in

1. heav-en.   2. heav-en.

I've been wait-ing for_ so long for some-thing_ to ar-rive; for love to come a-long. Now our dreams are com-in' true,

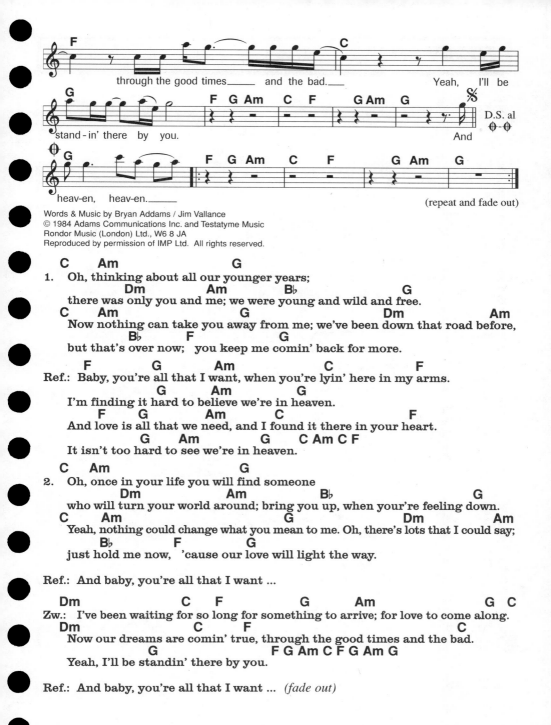

through the good times____ and the bad.__   Yeah,   I'll be

stand-in' there by you.   And

D.S. al

heav-en,   heav-en.____   (repeat and fade out)

Words & Music by Bryan Addams / Jim Vallance
© 1984 Adams Communications Inc. and Testatyme Music
Rondor Music (London) Ltd., W6 8 JA
Reproduced by permission of IMP Ltd. All rights reserved.

    C   **Am**   **G**
1. Oh, thinking about all our younger years;
        Dm   **Am**   **Bb**   **G**
   there was only you and me; we were young and wild and free.
   C   **Am**   **G**   **Dm**   **Am**
   Now nothing can take you away from me; we've been down that road before,
      Bb   **F**   **G**
   but that's over now; you keep me comin' back for more.

     F   **G**   **Am**   **C**   **F**
Ref.: Baby, you're all that I want, when you're lyin' here in my arms.
             G   **Am**   **G**
   I'm finding it hard to believe we're in heaven.
     F   **G**   **Am**   **C**   **F**
   And love is all that we need, and I found it there in your heart.
          G   **Am**   **G**   **C Am C F**
   It isn't too hard to see we're in heaven.

   C   **Am**   **G**
2. Oh, once in your life you will find someone
        Dm   **Am**   **Bb**   **G**
   who will turn your world around; bring you up, when your're feeling down.
   C   **Am**   **G**   **Dm**   **Am**
   Yeah, nothing could change what you mean to me. Oh, there's lots that I could say;
      Bb   **F**   **G**
   just hold me now,   'cause our love will light the way.

Ref.: And baby, you're all that I want ...

   Dm   **C**   **F**   **G**   **Am**   **G**   **C**
Zw.: I've been waiting for so long for something to arrive; for love to come along.
   Dm   **C**   **F**   **C**
   Now our dreams are comin' true, through the good times and the bad.
        G   **F G Am C F G Am G**
   Yeah, I'll be standin' there by you.

Ref.: And baby, you're all that I want ... *(fade out)*

HELP!

♩ | 192 | 8 Beat

Em Help! I need some-bod-y, **C** help! Not just a-ny-bod — y,

A7 help! You know I need some-one, **D7** help!_____

D When I___ was young-er so___ much young-er than___ to — day, **F#m**

Bm I nev-er need-ed an-y-bod — y's **G** help **C** in a-ny **D** way.___

But now these days are gone I'm not so self as-sured,_____ **F#m**

Bm now I find I've changed my mind, **G** I've o **C** -pened up **D** the doors.

Em Help me if you can,___ I'm feel-ing down,_____ and I do___

C ap — pre — ci — ate___ you be-ing round._____

A7 Help me get___ my feet back on the ground._____ Won't you please, **D**

please help me. | 1.+ 2. || 3. me. **Bm** Help me,___ **D** help me! ___ **Bm** Ooh

Words & Music by John Lennon & Paul McCartney
© 1965 by Northern Songs
All Rights Reserved. International Copyright Secured.

```
      Em                      C
Help! I need somebody, help! Not just anybody,
      A7                         D7
help! You know I need someone, help!

      D                        F#m
1.    When I was younger, so much younger than today,
      Bm                     G     C    D
      I never needed anybody's help in any way.
                              F#m
      But now these days are gone, I'm not so self assured,
      Bm                          G     C      D
      now I find I've changed my mind, I've opened up the doors.

        Em                            C
Ref.: Help me, if you can, I'm feeling down, and I do appreciate you being round.
        A7                              D
      Help me get my feet back on the ground. Won't you please, please help me.

      D                        F#m
2.    And now my life has changed in oh so many ways,
      Bm                     G     C     D
      my independence seems to vanish in the haze,
                            F#m
      but ev'ry now and then I feel so insecure,
      Bm                       G     C      D
      I know that I just need you like I've never done before.

        Em                            C
Ref.: Help me if you can, I'm feeling down, and I do appreciate you being round.
        A7                              D
      Help me get my feet back on the ground. Won't you please, please help me.

      D                        F#m
3.    When I was younger, so much younger than today,
      Bm                     G     C    D
      I never needed anybody's help in any way.
                              F#m
      But now these days are gone, I'm not so self-assured,
      Bm                          G     C      D
      now I find I've changed my mind, I've opened up the doors.

        Em                            C
Ref.: Help me if you can, I'm feeling down, and I do appreciate you being round.
        A7                              D
      Help me get my feet back on the ground. Won't you please, please help me.
            Bm        D  Bm
      Help me, help me! Ooh
```

HEY BABY

♩ | 135 | Techno-Pop

gespr.: Okay, senoritas y caballeros, ladies and gentlemen, meine Damen und Herren. Hey babies of the seventies! Okay, put your hands up in the air, die Hände in die Höh'! And everybody sing now!

Hey,_____ hey__ Ba - by! Uh!

Ah! I wan-na know_____ if you'll be my girl,

__ two, three, four, five, six se - ven, eight! Hey,_____ hey__ Ba -

by! Uh! Ah! I wan-na know_____ if you'll be my girl,

__ When I saw you walk-ing down the street

I said that's the kind of girl I'd__ like to meet.__ She's so pret-ty, Lord

__ she's fine__ I'm gon-na make her mine,__ oh mine.__ D.S. al ⊕·⊕

When you turn and walk a - way_ that's when I want to say_

come on, ba - by, give me a whirl_ I wan-na know I

wan-na know_____ I wan-na know if you'll be my girl.__ D.S. al ⊕ (3x, fade)

102

Words & Music by Margaret Cobb / Bruce Channel
© 1961 by Le Bill Music, Texas, USA. The Peter Maurice Music Co. Ltd., London, for The British Empire/Commonwealth of
Nations and Europe except Canada & Australasia
Für D/A/CH: Masterphon Musikverlag GmbH, Bergisch Gladbach

*gespr.: Okay, senoritas y caballeros, ladies and gentlemen, meine Damen und Herren.
Hey babies of the seventies! Okay, put your hands up in the air, die Hände in die Höh'!
And everybody sing now!*

      G Em C D G   Em Am D   G Em Am   D   G
Ref.: Hey   Baby! Uh! Ah! I wanna know   if you'll be my girl,
    Em   Am   D
two, three, four, five, six, seven, eight!

      G Em C D G   Em Am D   G Em Am   D   G
Hey   Baby! Uh! Ah! I wanna know   if you'll be my girl.

   C
1.   When I saw you walking down the street
   G
   I said that's the kind of girl I'd like to meet.
   C
   She's so pretty, Lord, she's fine,
   D
   I'm gonna make her mine, oh mine.

Ref.: Hey Baby! Uh! Ah! I wanna know ...

   E7
2.   When you turn and walk away
   A7
   that's when I want to say,
   D7
   come on, baby, give me a whirl,
   G
   I wanna know, I wanna know
   E7
   When you turn and walk away
   A7
   that's when I want to say,
   D7
   come on, baby, give me a whirl,
   G
   I wanna know if you'll be my girl.

Ref.: Hey Baby! Uh! Ah! I wanna know ... *(3x and fade)*

HEY JUDE

♩ 76 | Slow-Beat

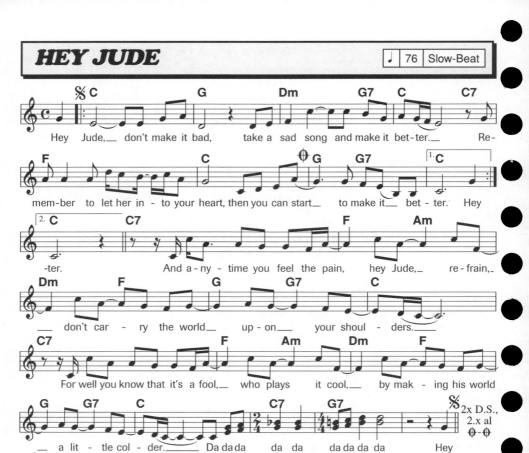

Words & Music by John Lennon & Paul McCartney

1.
      C   G   Dm   G7   C   C7
Hey Jude, don't make it bad, take a sad song and make it better.
      F   C   G   G7   C
Remember, to let her into your heart, then you can start to make it better.

2.
      C   G   Dm   G7   C   C7
Hey Jude, don't be afraid, you were made to go out and get her.
      F   C   G   G7   C
The minute you let her under your skin, then you begin to make it better.

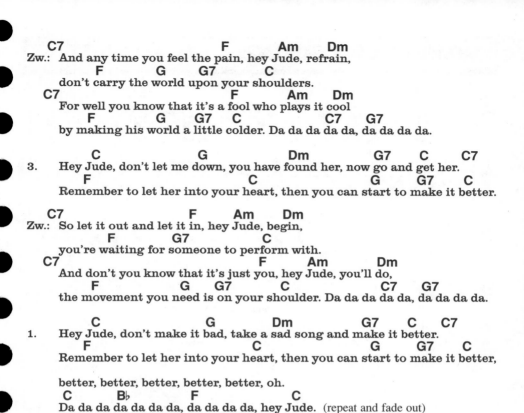

    C7   F   Am   Dm
Zw.: And any time you feel the pain, hey Jude, refrain,
           F   G   G7   C
      don't carry the world upon your shoulders.
    C7   F   Am   Dm
      For well you know that it's a fool who plays it cool
           F   G   G7   C   C7   G7
      by making his world a little colder. Da da da da da, da da da da.

           C   G   Dm   G7   C   C7
3.   Hey Jude, don't let me down, you have found her, now go and get her.
        F   C   G   G7   C
      Remember to let her into your heart, then you can start to make it better.

    C7   F   Am   Dm
Zw.: So let it out and let it in, hey Jude, begin,
           F   G7   C
      you're waiting for someone to perform with.
    C7   F   Am   Dm
      And don't you know that it's just you, hey Jude, you'll do,
           F   G   G7   C   C7   G7
      the movement you need is on your shoulder. Da da da da da, da da da da.

           C   G   Dm   G7   C   C7
1.   Hey Jude, don't make it bad, take a sad song and make it better.
        F   C   G   G7   C
      Remember to let her into your heart, then you can start to make it better,

      better, better, better, better, better, oh.
     C   B♭   F   C
      Da da da da da da da, da da da da, hey Jude. (repeat and fade out)

HOMEWARD BOUND

Words & Music by Paul Simon
© 1966 Paul Simon
All Rights Reserved. International Copyright Secured.

1.
      G   **Bm**   **Dm**   **E7**

I'm sittin' in the railway station, got a ticket for my destination. Hm

Am   **F**

On a tour of one-night stands, my suitcase and guitar in hand

  G   **D7**   **G**

and every step is neatly planned for a poet and a one-man band.

<pre>
          G   C   G   C
Ref.: Homeward bound, I wish I was homeward bound,
          G   Am   G   Am
      home, where my thought's escaping, home, where my music's playing,
          G   Am   D7   G
      home, where my love lies waiting silently for me.

          G   Bm   Dm   E7
2.   Ev'ry day's an endless stream of cigarettes and magazines. Hm
            Am   F
      And each town looks the same to me, the movies and the factories
            G   D7   G
      and ev'ry stranger's face I see reminds me that I long to be

          G   C   G   C
Ref.: Homeward bound, I wish I was homeward bound,
          G   Am   G   Am
      home, where my thought's escaping, home, where my music's playing,
          G   Am   D7   G
      home, where my love lies waiting silently for me.

          G   Bm   Dm   E7
3.   Tonight I'll sing my song again, I'll play the game and pretend. Hm
            Am   F
      But all my words come back to me in shades of mediocrity
            G   D7   G
      like emptiness in harmony, I need someone to comfort me.

          G   C   G   C
Ref.: Homeward bound, I wish I was homeward bound,
          G   Am   G   Am
      home, where my thought's escaping, home, where my music's playing,
          G   Am   D7   G
      home, where my love lies waiting silently for me.
</pre>

HOUSE OF THE RISING SUN

♩. 72 | Blues

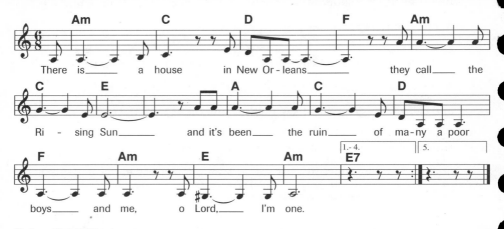

There is___ a house in New Or-leans___ they call___ the Ri - sing Sun___ and it's been___ the ruin___ of ma-ny a poor boys___ and me, o Lord,___ I'm one.

Musik und Text: Traditional

		Am	C	D	F	Am	C	E
1.	There is a house in New Orleans, they call the Rising Sun.							

           Am   C   D   F   Am   E   Am E7
And it's been the ruin of many a poor boys, and me, o Lord, I'm one.

           Am   C   D   F   Am   C   E
2. My mother was a tailor, she sewed my new blue jeans.

           Am C   D   F   Am   E   Am E7
My father was a gamblin' man way down in New Orleans.

           Am   C   D   F   Am   C   E
3. The only thing a gambler needs is a suitcase and a trunk.

           Am C   D F   Am   E   Am E7
And the only time that he's satisfied, is when he's all a-drunk.

           Am   C   D   F   Am   C   E
4. I've got one foot on the platform and the other's on the train.

           Am C   D   F   Am   E   Am E7
I'm goin' back to New Orleans to wear that ball and chain.

             Am   C   D   F Am   C   E
5. Now, mothers, tell your children: Not' do, what I have done.

           Am   C   D   F   Am   E   Am
To spend your lives in sin and misery, in the house of the Rising Sun.

HYMN

♩ 72 | Ballade

Val-ley's deep and the moun-tain so high, if you
wan-na see God you got-ta move on the oth-er side.
You stand up there with your head in the clouds, don't
try to fly, you know you might not come down,— don't
try to fly near God,— you might not come down.—

Words & Music by John Lees

1.
E   **A**   **E**
Valley's deep and the mountain so high.
     A   **E**
If you wanna see God, you gotta move on the other side.
                   A   **E**
You stand up there with your head in the clouds,
     A   **E**
don't try to fly, you know you might not come down,
     A   **E**
don't try to fly near God, you might not come down.

2. **E**‖: Jesus came down from heaven to earth, the **A** people **E** said **A** it was virgin birth, :‖ **E**
         A   **E**
the people said it was - a virgin birth.

3. **E**‖: He told great stories of the **A** Lord, **E** and **A** said he was the savior of us all. :‖ **E**
          A   **E**
and said he was the savior - of us all.

4. **E** For this we killed him, nailed him up **A** high. **E** He **A** rose again as to ask us why. **E**
              A   **E**
Then he ascended into the sky, as if to say in God alone you soar,
     A   **E**
as if to say in God - alone we fly.   Valley's deep ... (2x)

I SHOULD HAVE KNOWN BETTER

♩=160 Beat

Words & Music by John Lennon & Paul McCartney
© 1964 Northern Songs
All Rights Reserved. International Copyright Secured.

```
         C G C  G                    C         G      C
1.  I       should have known better with a girl like you,
    G              C          G       Am    F           G
    that I would love ev'rything that you do; and I do, hey, hey, hey,
         C G C  G
    and I do.      Wo wo


         C G C G          C          G        C
2.  I       never realized what a kiss could be.
    G            C    G      Am           F              E7
    This could only happen to me; can't you see? Can't you see?
```

```
Am                 F                C          E7
   That when I tell you that I love you, oh!
Am              C                           C7
   You're gonna say you love me, too, hoo hoo hoo, oh.
F           G                C          Am
   And when I ask you to be mine ah-ha-hine,
F              G7              C G C  G
   you're gonna say you love me, too.     So-o


   C G C  G                      C           G       C
3. I       should have realized a lot of things before.
   G         C            G       Am         F          G7
   If this is love, you gotta give me more; give me more, hey, hey, hey,
                C  G C  G
   give me more.     So-o


   C G C G        C           G        C
4. I       never realized what a kiss could be.
   G          C    G      Am             F          E7
   This could only happen to me; can't you see? Can't you see?


Am                 F                C          E7
   That when I tell you that I love you, oh!
Am              C                           C7
   You're gonna say you love me, too, hoo hoo hoo, oh.
F           G                C          Am
   And when I ask you to be mine ah-ha-hine,
F              G7              C G C    G        C
   you're gonna say you love me, too.      You love me, too. (fade out)
```

I WILL SURVIVE

♩ 108 | Medium Beat

Am At first I was a-fraid,__ I was pet-ri-fied,__ kept think-in'

G I could nev-er live__ with-out you by my side; **C** but then I

F spent so man-y nights think-in' how you did me wrong and I grew **Bm**

E strong and I learned how to get a-long.__ And so you're

℅ Am back from out-er space, **Dm** I just walked

G in to find_ you here with that sad look up-on your face. **C** I should have changed

F __ that stu-pid lock,__ I should have made_ you leave your key_ if I'd have known **Bm**

E __ for just_ one sec-ond you'd be back to both-er me.__ Go on now,

Am go, walk out the door,__ **Dm** just turn a-round

G __ now__ 'cause you're not wel-come an-y more.__ **C**

F Weren't you the one_ who tried to hurt_ me with good-bye, **Bm** did I crum-

E ble,__ did you think I'd lay down_ and die? Oh no, not

112

Words & Music by Dino Fekaris & Freddie Perren
© 1978 Perren-Vibes Music Company & PolyGram International Publishing Inc., USA
Universal Music Publishing Ltd., 77 Fulham Palace Road, London W6
All Rights Reserved. International Copyright Secured.

113

1.   **Am**   **Dm**
    At first I was afraid, I was petrified,
               G   **C**
    kept thinkin' I could never live without you by my side;
        F   **Bm**
    but then I spent so many nights thinkin' how you did me wrong
        E
    and I grew strong and I learned how to get along.
                  Am   **Dm**
    And now you're back from outer space,
               G   **C**
    I just walked in to find you here with that sad look upon your face.
        F   **Bm**
    I should have changed that stupid lock, I should have made you leave the key
        E
    if I'd 've known for just one second you'd be back to bother me.
               Am   **Dm**
    Go on now, go, walk out the door,
               G   **C**
    just turn around now, 'cause you're not welcome any more.
  F   **Bm**
    Weren't you the one who tried to hurt me with good-bye,
        E
    did I crumble, did you think I'd lay down and die?

              Am   **Dm**
Ref.: Oh no, not I, I will survive,
               G   **C**
    oh, as long as I know how to love, I know I'll stay alive;
        F   **Bm**
    I've got all my life to live, I've got all my love to give
               E   **Am Dm G C F Bm E E7**
    and I'll survive, I will survive. Hey, hey. *(instr.)*

               Am   **Dm**
2.   It took all the strength I had not to fall apart,
               G   **C**
    kept tryin' hard to mend the pieces of my broken heart,
        F   **Bm**
    and I spent oh so many nights just feelin' sorry for myself,
        E
    I used to cry, but now I hold my head up high,
               Am   **Dm**
    and you see me, somebody new,
               G   **C**
    I'm not that chained up little person still in love with you,
        F   **Bm**
    and so you feel like droppin' in and just expect me to be free,
        E
    now I'm savin' all my lovin' for someone who's lovin' me.
               Am   **Dm**
    Go on now, go, walk out the door ...

              Am   **Dm**   **E**   **Am Dm Am**
Ref.: Oh no, not I, I will survive ... I will survive, I'll survive.

I'M WALKIN'

♩ 176 | Rock 'n' Roll

I'm walk-in', ___ yes in-deed ___ and I'm talk-in' ___ 'bout
you and me, ___ I'm hop-in' ___ that you'll come ___ back to me ___ hm. ___
___ Yes I'm lone-ly ___ as I can be, ___ I'm wait-ing ___ for your
com-pa-ny, ___ I'm hop-in' ___ that you'll come back to me. ___
What you gon-na do when the well runs dry? You're gon-na run a-
way and hide. I'm gon-na run right by your side for
you pret-ty ba-by I'll e-ven die. ___ I'm walk-in', ___
yes in-deed ___ and I'm talk-in' ___ 'bout you and me, ___ I'm
hop-in' ___ that you'll come ___ back to me ___ hm. ___

Words & Music by Dave Bartholomew / Antoine Domino
© 1957 by Reeve Music Co. Inc.
Für Deutschland, Österreich und die Schweiz: Rolf Budde Musikverlag GmbH, Berlin

    A   **D**
I'm walkin', yes indeed, and I'm talkin' 'bout you and me,
    A   **E**   **A**
I'm hopin' that you'll come back to me hm. Yes, I'm lonely as can be,
 D   **A**   **E**   **A**
I'm waiting for your company, I'm hopin' that you'll come back to me.
 D   **A**   **D**   **A**
What you gonna do, when the well runs dry? You're gonna run away and hide.
 D   **A**   **B7**   **E7**   **A**
I'm gonna run right by your side for you, pretty baby, I'll even die. I'm walkin' ...

IN THE GHETTO

♩ | 80 | Medium Beat

As the snow___ flies___ on a

cold an grey Chi - ca - go morn - in', a poor lit - tle ba - by child is born in the

Ghet-to.___ And his ma-ma cries,___ 'cause if

there's one thing she does - n't need, it's an - oth - er hun - gry mouth to feed in the

Ghet-to.___ (Fine) Peo - ple, don't you un - der-stand, the child needs a

hel - ping hand,___ or he'll grow to be an an - gry young man some -

day. Take a look at you and me, are we too

blind___ to see,___ or do we simp - ly turn our heads and look the oth - er

way? Well, the world___ turns___ and a

And then one night, in des-per-a - tion a young man breaks a-way. He

buys a gun,— steals a car,— tries to run,— but he don't get far and his

ma - ma cries.— As a

Words & Music by Mac Davis

       C   Em
1.   As the snow flies on a cold and grey Chicago mornin',
       F   G7   C
   a poor little baby child is born in the Ghetto.
                         Em
   And his mama cries, 'cause if there's one thing she doesn't need,
      F   G7   C
   it's another hungry mouth to feed in the Ghetto.

                 G   F   C
Zw.: People, don't you understand, the child needs a helping hand,
      F   G7   C
   or he'll grow to be an angry young man some day.
                 G   F   C
   Take a look at you and me, are we too blind to see,
      F   Em   Dm   G7
   or do we simply turn our heads and look the other way?

      C   Em
2. Well, the world turns and a hungry little boy with the runny nose
       F   G7   C
   plays in the street, as the cold wind blows in the Ghetto.
                         Em
   And his hunger burns, and he starts to roam the streets at night
        F   G7   C
   and he learns how to steal and he learns how to fight in the Ghetto.

           G   F   C
Zw.: And then one night, in desperation a young man breaks away.
      F   Em   Dm   G7
   He buys a gun, steals a car, tries to run, but he don't get far

      C   Em
3. and his mama cries. As a crowd gathers 'round an angry young man,
       F   G7   C
   face down in the street with a gun in his hand, in the Ghetto.
                         Em
   And as her young man dies, on a cold and grey Chicago mornin',
      F   G7   C
   another little baby child is born in the Ghetto.

IT'S MY LIFE

♩ 118 | Medium Beat

(life)

This ain't a song_ for the bro - ken heart - ed, a si - lent prayer for faith de - part - ed, and I ain't gon - na be just a face in the crowd, you're gon - na hear my voice when I shout it out loud.

It's my_ life, it's now or nev - er, an' I ain't gon - na live for - ev - er,_ I just wan - na live when I'm_ a - live._

It's my_ life. My heart is like an o - pen high - way, like Frank-ie said I did it my way,_ I just wan - na live when I'm_ a - live._ It's my life._

Ba - by stand tall when they're call - ing you out,_ don't bend, don't break, ba - by don't back down. It's my_ life, it's now_ or nev - er,

Words & Music by Jon Bon Jovi / Richie Sambora / Max Martin
© 2000 Bon Jovi Publishing / Aggressive Music / Universal Music Publishing Ltd., 77 Fulham Palace Road,
London W6 (66,67%) / Zomba Music Publishers Ltd., 165-167 High Road, London NW10 (33,33%)
All Rights Reserved. International Copyright Secured.

Am
1. This ain't a song for the broken hearted,
   a silent prayer for the faith departed,
   and I ain't gonna be just a face in the crowd,
        Dm
   You're gonna hear my voice, when I cry it out loud.

       Am   **F**
Ref.: It's my life, it's now or never
   C   **G**
   an' I ain't gonna live forever,
Am   **F**   **G**
   I just wanna live when I'm alive.
       Am   **F**
   It's my life. My heart is like an open highway,
   C   **G**
   like Frankie said I did it my way,
Am   **F**   **G**   **Am**
   I just wanna live when I'm alive. It's my life.

Am
2. This is for the ones who stood their ground,
   for Tommy and Gina who never backed down,
   tomorrow's getting harder, make no mistake,
        Dm
   luck ain't even luck you gotta make your own breaks.

Ref.: It's my life, it's now or never ...

      Am
Zw.: Baby stand tall, when they're calling you out,
     don't bend, don't break, baby don't back down.

Ref.: It's my life, it's now or never ... *(2x)*

IMAGINE

♩ 80 | Ballade

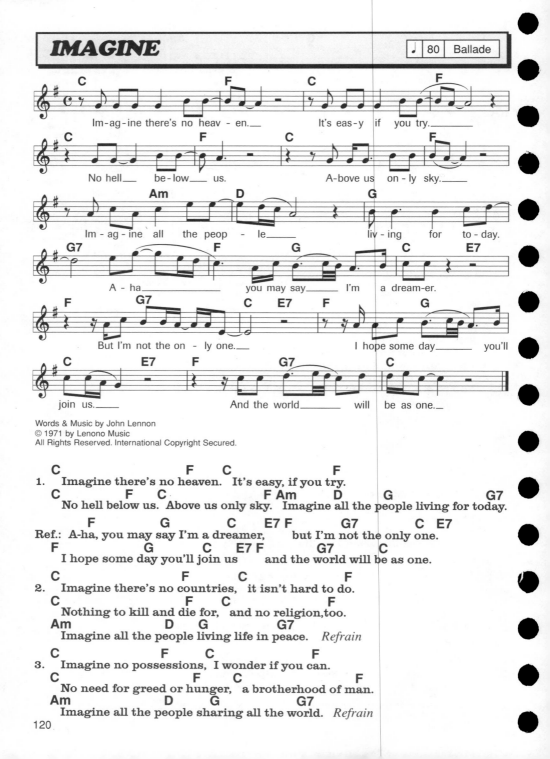

    C   F   C   F

1. Imagine there's no heaven. It's easy, if you try.

   C   F   C   F Am   D   G   G7

    No hell below us. Above us only sky. Imagine all the people living for today.

      F   G   C   E7 F   G7   C E7

Ref.: A-ha, you may say I'm a dreamer,   but I'm not the only one.

   F   G   C   E7 F   G7   C

    I hope some day you'll join us   and the world will be as one.

   C   F   C   F

2. Imagine there's no countries, it isn't hard to do.

   C   F   C   F

    Nothing to kill and die for, and no religion,too.

Am   D   G   G7

    Imagine all the people living life in peace.   *Refrain*

   C   F   C   F

3. Imagine no possessions, I wonder if you can.

   C   F   C   F

    No need for greed or hunger, a brotherhood of man.

Am   D   G   G7

    Imagine all the people sharing all the world.   *Refrain*

JOHNNY B.

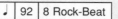

Words & Music by Rob Hyman / Eric Bazillian / Rick Chertoff
© Universal/Hobbler Music/Dub Notes Music/ Human Boy Music

```
            Am          C      Am           C
1.   It's a sleepless night, she's calling your name,
            Am      C    Am           C
     it's a lonely ride, I know how you want her.
     Dm          F          Dm          F
     Again and again you're chasin' a dream, yeah,
            Am          C          Dm          F
     but Johnny my friend, oh, she's not what she seems.

               Am      F          G
Ref.: Johnny B., how much there is to see,
          Am      F      G      Am
     just open your eyes and listen to me.
                               F          G
     Straight ahead, a green light turns to red,
          Am          F G      Am
     oh, why can't you see, oh, Johnny B.?
```

121

                Am   **C**   **Am**   **C**
2.   And when you drive her home, is she sittin' real close,
             Am   **C**   **Am**   **C**
    does she make you weak, well, that's the way that she wants you,
              Dm   **F**   **Dm**   **F**
    you're strong out again, she's taken you over,
            Am **C**   **Dm**   **F**
    you've been here before, why can't you let go?

              Am   **F**   **G**
Ref.: Johnny B., how much there is to see ...
              Am   **C**   **Am**   **C**
3.   And when she calls your name, my sweet Johnny B.,
             Am   **C**   **Am**   **C**
    you can drive all night and you know she'll be waiting
       Dm   **F**   **Dm**   **F**
    to love you again, her kiss is her poison,
      Am **C**   **Dm**   **F**
    forever inside you, wherever you go.   *Ref.*

KNOCKIN' ON HEAVEN'S DOOR ♩ 64 Slow

  G   **D**   **Am G**   **D**   **C**
1.   Mother, take this badge from me.   I can't use it anymore.
  G   **D**   **Am G**   **D**   **C**
   It's getting dark, too dark to see,   feels like I'm knockin' on heaven's door.

      G   **D**   **Am**
Ref.: Knock, knock, knockin' on heaven's door.
      G   **D**   **C**
   Knock, knock, knockin' on heaven's door.
      G   **D**   **Am**
   Knock, knock, knockin' on heaven's door.
      G   **D**   **C**   **G D Am G D C**
   Knock, knock, knockin' on heaven's door.
  G   **D**   **Am G**   **D**   **C**
2.   Mama, put those guns to the ground 'cause I can't shoot them anymore.
  G   **D**   **Am G**   **D**   **C**
   That cold black cloud is comin' down,   feels like I'm knockin' on heaven's door.

      G   **D**   **Am**
Ref.: Knock, knock, knockin' on heaven's door ...

  G   **D**   **Am G**   **D**   **C**
3.   Mama, what's about from my face,   I can't see it anymore.
  G   **D**   **Am G**   **D**   **C**
   It's a feeling that I just can't train,   I feel like I'm knockin' on heaven's door.

      G   **D**   **Am**
Ref.: Knock, knock, knockin' on heaven's door.
      G   **D**   **C**
   Knock, knock, knockin' on heaven's door.
      G   **D**   **Am**
   Knock, knock, knockin' on heaven's door.
      G   **D**   **C**   **G D Am G D C G**
   Knock, knock, knockin' on heaven's door.

Words & Music by Bob Dylan
© 1973 Ram's Horn Music, USA
This arrangement © 2000 Ram's Horn Music
All Rights Reserved. International Copyright Secured.

LAY DOWN SALLY

♩ 144 | Shuffle

There is noth-ing that_ is wrong in want-ing you_ to stay_ here_ with me. I know you've got_ some-where_ to go,_ but won't you make_ your-self_ at home and stay with me?_ And don't you ev-er leave. Lay down, Sal-ly, and rest you in_ my arms._ Don't you think you want_ some-one_ to talk to? Lay down, Sal-ly, no need to leave so soon. I've been try-ing all_ night long_ just to talk to you._ The talk to you._ I've been try-ing all_ night long_ just to talk to you._

Words & Music by Eric Clapton, Marcy Levy & George Terry
© 1978 by E. C. MUSIC LTD./THROAT MUSIC LTD./WARNER/CHAPPELL INTERNATIONAL MUSIC LTD., London
Für Deutschland, US und osteuropäische Länder: NEUE WELT MUSIKVERLAG GMBH, München/
CHAPPELL & CO GMBH, Hamburg
© 1977 & 1999 Eric Clapton
All Rights Reserved. International Copyright Secured.

```
         G7                                                        C
1.   There is nothing that is wrong in wanting you to stay here with me.
         G7
     I know you've got somewhere to go,
                                              C
     but won't you make yourself at home and stay with me?
                 D
     And don't you ever leave.

         G             C
Ref.: Lay down, Sally, and rest you in my arms.
         D                                     G        D7
     Don't you think you want someone to talk to?
     G             C
     Lay down, Sally, no need to leave so soon.
     D                             G
     I've been trying all night long just to talk to you.


         G7                                                        C
2.   The sun ain't nearly on the rise, and we still got the moon and stars above.
     G7
     Underneath the velvet skies
                              C
     love is all that matters. Won't you stay with me?
                 D
     And don't you ever leave.


         G             C
Ref.: Lay down, Sally, and rest you in my arms ...


         G7                                                        C
3.   I long to see the morning light colouring your face so dreamily.
         G7
     So don't you go and say good-bye;
                                  C
     you can lay your worries down and stay with me.
                 D
     And don't you ever leave.


         G             C
Ref.: Lay down, Sally, and rest you in my arms ...
```

LAYLA

Words & Music by Eric Clapton & Jim Gordon
© 1970 by E. C. MUSIC LTD./ THROAT MUSIC LTD.
Für Deutschland, GUS und osteuropäische Länder: NEUE WELT MUSIKVERLAG GMBH, München/
CHAPPELL & CO GMBH, Hamburg
© 1970, 1971 & 1998 by Eric Clapton
All Rights Reserved. International Copyright Secured.

     C#m   G#m C#m   D   E E7

1.   What will you do, when you get lonely   with nobody waiting by your side?

  A   E   A

   You've been running and hiding much too long,

F#m7   B   E

   you know it's just your foolish pride.

     A Dm Bb   C   Dm   Bb   C   Dm

Ref.: Layla,   you got me on my knees, Layla,   I'm begging darling, please,

       Bb C   Dm   Bb C

    Layla,   darling won't you ease my worried mind.

   C#m   G#m C#m   D   E   E7

2.   Tried to give you consolation,   your old man won't let you down.

   A   E   A F#m7   B   E

     Like a fool I fell in love with you,   turned the whole world upside down.

   A Dm Bb   C   Dm   Bb   C   Dm

Ref.: Layla,   you got me on my knees, Layla, I'm begging darling, please,

       Bb C   Dm   Bb C

     Layla,   darling won't you ease my worried mind.

   C#m   G#m C#m   D   E   E7

3.   Let's make the best of the situation,   before I finally go insane.

   A   E   A F#m7   B   E

     Please, don't say we'll never find a way   and tell me all my love's in vain.

   A Dm Bb   C   Dm   Bb   C   Dm

Ref.: Layla,   you got me on my knees, Layla, I'm begging darling, please,

       Bb C   Dm   Bb C

     Layla,   darling won't you ease my worried mind.

   Dm   Bb   C   Dm   Bb   C   Dm

     Layla,   you got me on my knees, Layla, I'm begging darling, please ...

                                                 (fade out)

LEMON TREE

♩ 144 | Foxtrot

I'm sit-ting here in a bor-ing room. it's just a-no-ther rai-ny Sun-day af-ter-noon. I'm wast-ing my time I got no-thing to do.__ I'm hang-ing a-round, I'm wait-ing for you.__ But no-thing e-ver hap-pens__ __ and I won - der.__ I'm won-der how, I won-der why,__ yes-ter-day you told me 'bout the blue, blue sky__ and all __ that I__ can see__ is just a yel-low lem-on tree.__ I'm turn-ing my head__ up and down, I'm turn-ing, turn-ing, turn-ing, turn-ing, turn-ing a-round. And all__ that I__ can see__ is just a yel-low lem-on tree.__ Sing! dab, da da da__ dab di dab da,__ da da da__ dab di dab da,__ dab dib di da.__ I'm

I - so - la - tion__ is not good for me. I - so - la - tion,__ I don't want to sit on a lem-on tree. I'm

128

and all___ that I___ can see,___ and all___ that I___ can see___ ___ is just a yel - low lem - on tree.___

Words & Music by Peter Freudenthaler / Volker Hinkel
© by EMI MMC MUSIKVERLAG GmbH & Co. KG, Hamburg

| Bm   F#m   Bm   F#m
1. I'm sitting here in a boring room. It's just another rainy Sunday afternoon.
| Bm   F#m   Bm   F#m
I'm wasting my time, I got nothing to do. I'm hanging around, I'm waiting for you.
| Em   F#m   Bm F#m
But nothing ever happens – and I wonder.

| Bm   F#m   Bm   F#m
2. I'm driving around in my car, I'm driving too fast, I'm driving too far.
| Bm   F#m   Bm   F#m
I'd like to change my point of view. I feel so lonely, I'm waiting for you.
| Em   F#m   Bm F#m
But nothing ever happens – and I wonder.

| D   A   Bm   F#m
Ref.: I wonder how, I wonder why, yesterday you told me 'bout the blue, blue sky
| G   A   D   A
and all that I can see is just a yellow lemon tree.
| D   A   Bm
I'm turning my head up and down. I'm turning, turning, turning turning,
| F#m   G   E   A7
turning around. And all that I can see is just a yellow lemon tree. Sing!
| Bm F#m   Bm   F#m   Em   F#m   Bm
dab – da da da dab di dab da, – da da da dab di dab da, – dab dib di da.

3. = 1.

| Bm   F#m   Bm   F#m
4. I'm sitting here, I miss the power, I'd like to go out taking a shower,
| Bm   F#m   Bm   F#m
but there's a heavy cloud inside my head, feel so tired, put myself into bed
| Em   F#m   Bm F#m
where nothing ever happens – and I wonder.

| F#7   Bm   A7   D   F#7
Zw.: Isolation is not good for me. – Isolation, I don't want to   sit on a lemon tree.

| Bm   F#m   Bm   F#m
5. I'm steppin' around in the desert of joy, Baby, anyhow I'll get another toy
| Em   F#m   Bm   F#m Bm
and everything will happen – and you'll wonder.

Ref.: I wonder how ... and I wonder, I wonder,

| D   A   Bm   F#m
Ref.: I wonder how, I wonder why, yesterday you told me 'bout the blue, blue sky
| G   A   G   A   D
||:and all that I can see:|| and all that I can see is just a yellow lemon tree.

129

LET IT BE

♩ 72 Slow

When I find my-self in times of trou-ble Mo-ther Ma - ry comes to me
speak-ing words of wis - dom, let it be.___ And in my hour of dark - ness she is
stand-ing right in front of me speak-ing words of wis - dom, let it be.___ Let it be,
___ let it be,___ let it be,___ let it be, whis-per words of wis - dom let it be.
___ And when the bro - ken heart-ed peo-ple liv-ing in the world a-gree,
there will be an an - swer, let it be.___ For though they may be part - ed there is
still a chance that they will see, there will be an an - swer, let it be.___ Let it be,
___ let it be,___ let it be,___ let it be. There will be an an - swer, let it be.
___ Let it be,___ let it be,___ let it be,___ let it be,___
whis-per words of wis - dom, let it be.___

	C	B♭	F	B♭	F	C	B♭	F	%

D.S. al ⊕-⊕

When I

B♭	F	Dm	C	B♭	F

Let it be,___ let it be,___ let it be,___ let it be,__

C	B♭ F	B♭	F	C B♭ F

whis-per words of wis - dom, let it be._____

Words & Music by John Lennon & Paul McCartney
© 1970 Northern Songs
All Rights Reserved. International Copyright Secured.

         F   **C**   **Dm**   **B♭**
1. When I find myself in times of trouble, Mother Mary comes to me
     F   **C**   **B♭ F Gm**
     speaking words of wisdom, let it be.
     F   **C**   **Dm**   **B♭**
     And in my hour of darkness she is standing right in front of me
     F   **C**   **B♭ F**
     speaking words of wisdom, let it be.
     Dm   **C**   **B♭**   **F**
Ref.: Let it be, let it be, let it be, let it be,
              C   **B♭ F**
     whisper words of wisdom, let it be.
     F   **C**   **Dm**   **B♭**
2. And when the broken hearted people living in the world agree,
     F   **C**   **B♭ F Gm**
     there will be an answer, let it be.
         F   **C**   **Dm**   **B♭**
     For though they may be parted, there is still a chance that they will see,
     F   **C**   **B♭ F**
     there will be an answer, let it be.
     Dm   **C**   **B♭**   **F**
Ref.: Let it be, let it be, let it be, let it be,
              C   **B♭ F**
     there will be an answer, let it be.
     Dm   **C**   **B♭**   **F**
     Let it be, let it be, let it be, let it be,
              C   **B♭ F**
     whisper words of wisdom, let it be.   (Wiederholung Strophe 1 + Refrain)
        F   **C**   **Dm**   **B♭**
3. And when the night is cloudy, there is still a light that shines on me,
     F   **C**   **B♭ F Gm**
     shine until tomorrow, let it be.
     F   **C**   **Dm**   **B♭**
     I wake up to the sound of music, Mother Mary comes to me,
     F   **C**   **B♭ F**
     speaking words of wisdom, let it be.
     Dm   **C**   **B♭**   **F**
Ref.: Let it be, let it be, let it be, let it be ...

LIVIN' ON A PRAYER

♩ 112 | Moderato Rock

(gespr.:) Once upon a time, not so long ago ...

Tom-my used to work on the docks,___ un-ion's been on strike. He's

down on his luck, it's tough,___ so tough.___

Gi - na works the din - er all day___ work-ing for her man. She

brings home her pay for love,___ for love.___

She says we've got to hold on___ to what we've got,

does - n't make a diff' - rence if we make it or not. We've

got each oth - er and that's a lot for___ love.___ We'll give it a shot.

Wo,___ we're half - way there.___ Wo,___ liv - in' on a prayer.

Take my___ hand, we'll make it, I swear. Wo,___ liv - in' on a prayer.

132

Liv - in' on__ a prayer.____

Oh,_____ we've got to hold on__ read-y or__ not, you

live for the fight when it's all that you've got. Wo,_____ we're

half-way there. Wo,_____ liv - in' on a prayer. Take my hand and we'll

make it, I swear.__ Wo,_____ liv - in' on a prayer.__

Words & Music by Jon Bon Jovi, Richie Sambora & Desmond Child
© 1986 Bon Jovi Publishing / Universal Music Publishing Ltd., 77 Fulham Palace Road, London W6 (66,67%)
All Rights Reserved. International Copyright Secured.

Em C D Em   C   D   Em
(gespr.:) Once upon a time, not so long ago ...

Em
1. Tommy used to work on the docks, union's been on strike.
                           C   D   Em
He's down on his luck, it's tough,   so tough.

Gina works the diner all day, working for her man.
                       C   D
She brings home her pay for love,   for love. She says:

            C   D   **Em**
Ref.: We've got to hold on to what we've got,
     C   **D**   **Em**
doesn't make a diff'rence, if we make it or not.
      C D   **Em C**   **D**
We've got each other and that's a lot for love. We'll give it a shot.
Em C   **D**   **G D7**
Wo,   we're halfway there. Wo, livin' on a prayer.
Em   **C**   **D**   **G C D7**   **Em**
Take my hand, we'll make it, I swear. Wo,   livin' on a prayer.

      Em
2. Tommy's got his sixstring in hock,
                                                  C   D   Em
now he's holding in what he used to make it talk. So tough,   it's tough.

Gina dreams of running away; when she cries in the night,
                         C D
Tommy whispers: Baby, it's OK   some day.

            C D   **Em**
Ref.: We've got to hold on to what we've got,
     C   **D**   **Em**
doesn't make a diff'rence, if we make it or not.
        C D   **Em C**   **D**
We've got each other and that's a lot for love. We'll give it a shot.
Em C   **D**   **G D7**
Wo,   we're halfway there. Wo, livin' on a prayer.
Em   **C**   **D**   **G C D7**
Take my hand, we'll make it, I swear. Wo,   livin' on a prayer.
C   **Em C D G C D Em C D G C Em**
Livin' on a prayer. *(instr.)*
            C D   **Em D**
Oh, we've got to hold on, ready or not,
      C   **D**
you live for the fight, when it's all that you've got.
Gm E♭   **F**   **B♭ E♭ F7 Gm E♭ F B♭ E♭ F7**
Wo,   we're halfway there. Wo,   livin' on a prayer.
Gm   **E♭**   **F**   **B♭ E♭ F7**
Take my hand, we'll make it, I swear. Wo,   livin' on a prayer.

NOWHERE MAN

♩ 124 | Beat

He's a real no-where-man, sit-ting in his no-where land, mak-ing all his no-where plans for no-bo-dy.

Does-n't have a point of view, knows not where he's go-ing to, is-n't he a bit like you an' me? No-where man,

please li-sten, you don't know, what you're mis-sing, no-where man,

the world is at your com-mand.

Words & Music by John Lennon & Paul McCartney
© 1965 Northern Songs
All Rights Reserved. International Copyright Secured.

```
              D          A          G          D
Intro: He's a real nowhere man, sitting in his nowhere land,
         G          Gm             D
       making all his nowhere plans for nobody.
              D          A          G          D
1.     Doesn't have a point of view, knows not where he's going to,
         G     Gm        D
       isn't he a bit like you and me?
                  F#m         G             F#m             G
Ref. 1: Nowhere man, please listen, you don't know, what you're missing,
                  F#m   G                     A7
        nowhere man, the world is at your command.
              D          A          G          D
2.     He's as blind as he can be, just sees what he wants to see,
         G          Gm         D
       nowhere man, can you see me at all?
                  F#m         G             F#m         G
Ref. 2: Nowhere man, don't worry, take your time, don't hurry
                  F#m   G                         A7
        leave it all till somebody else lends you a hand.  (Wdh. Str. 1, Ref. 1 + Intro)
```

135

MAMMA MIA

♩ 138 | Pop-Rock

I've been chea-ted by you   since I don't know when.

So   I made up my mind   it must come to an end.

Look   at   me   now,___   will   I   e - ver learn?   I don't know how,

but   I   sud-den - ly   lose___ con - trol.___   There's a fire___   with-in

___ my soul.___   Just   one   look and I can hear a bell ring,___   one more

look and I   for-get   ev' - ry - thing.___   Oh___   Mam-ma   mi - a

here   I   go   a-gain,___   my,   my,   how___   can   I   re-sist you?

Mam-ma   mi - a   does it show a - gain?   My,   my,   just___

___ how much I've missed you.   Yes,___   I've been bro - ken heart - ed,

blue___   since the day___   we   part - ed.   Why,   why,   did___

___ I   ev - er let you go?___   Mam-ma   mi - a,   now   I   real-ly know,

136

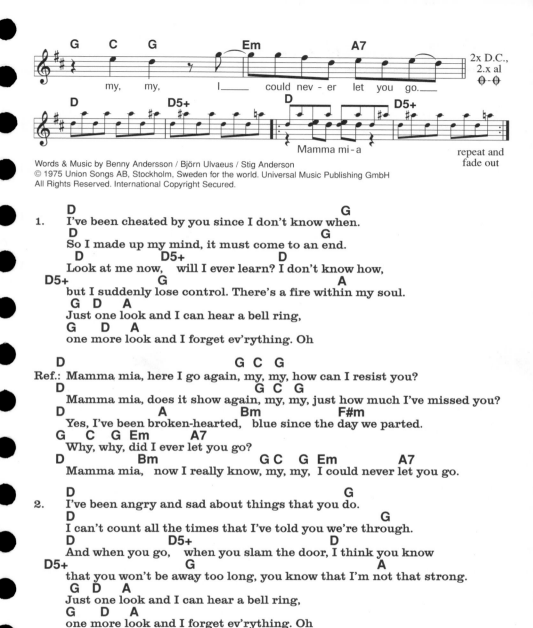

Mamma mi-a

repeat and
fade out

2x D.C.,
2.x al

```
       D                                    G
1.   I've been cheated by you since I don't know when.
       D                                    G
     So I made up my mind, it must come to an end.
       D          D5+          D
     Look at me now,   will I ever learn? I don't know how,
   D5+          G                              A
     but I suddenly lose control. There's a fire within my soul.
       G   D   A
     Just one look and I can hear a bell ring,
       G    D    A
     one more look and I forget ev'rything. Oh
```

```
     D                          G C G
Ref.: Mamma mia, here I go again, my, my, how can I resist you?
     D                          G C G
     Mamma mia, does it show again, my, my, just how much I've missed you?
     D          A         Bm            F#m
     Yes, I've been broken-hearted,   blue since the day we parted.
     G   C   G Em      A7
     Why, why, did I ever let you go?
     D          Bm            G C  G Em        A7
     Mamma mia,   now I really know, my, my, I could never let you go.
```

```
       D                                    G
2.   I've been angry and sad about things that you do.
       D                                    G
     I can't count all the times that I've told you we're through.
       D          D5+               D
     And when you go,   when you slam the door, I think you know
   D5+              G                              A
     that you won't be away too long, you know that I'm not that strong.
       G   D   A
     Just one look and I can hear a bell ring,
       G    D    A
     one more look and I forget ev'rything. Oh
```

Ref.: Mamma mia, here I go again ... I could never let you go. *(2x)*

Mamma mia, Mamma mia ... *(fade out)*

137

MR. TAMBOURINE MAN

♩ | 119 | Beat

Words & Music by Bob Dylan
© 1964 M. Witmark & Sons, USA
renewed 1992 Special Rider Music, USA
This arrangement © 2000 Special Rider Music
All Rights Reserved. International Copyright Secured.

```
          C            D              G              C
Ref.:  Hey, Mister Tambourine Man, play a song for me,
               G           C      Am        D
       I'm not sleepy and there is no place I'm goin' to.
          C            D              G              C
       Hey, Mister Tambourine Man, play a song for me
               G           C      Am        D        G
       in the jingle jungle mornin' I'll come followin' you.
```

```
                   C              D         G          C
1.   Though I know that evening's empire has returned into sand
        G           C
     vanished from my hand
           G              C      Am        D
     left me blindly here to stand but still not sleepin'!
          C            D              G          C
     My weariness amazes me, I'm branded on my feet,
        G            C
     I have no one to meet,
             G              C      Am        D
     and the ancient empty street's too dead for dreamin'.
```

Ref.: Hey, Mister Tambourine Man, play a song for me ...

2.   Take me on a trip upon your magic swirlin' ship,
     my senses have been stripped, my hands can't feel to grip,
     my toes too numb to step,
     wait only for my boot heels to be wand'rin'.
     I have no one to meet,
     and the ancient empty street's too dead for dreamin'.

Ref.: Hey, Mister Tambourine Man, play a song for me ...

3.   Though you might hear laughin', spinnin', swingin'
     madly across the sun, it's not aimed at anyone,
     it's just escaping on the run,
     and but for the sky there are no fences facin'.
     And if you hear vague traces of skippin' reels of rhyme
     to your Tambourine Man in time,
     it's just ragged the clown behind, I wouldn't pay it any mind,
     it's just a shadow you're seein' that he's chasin'.

Ref.: Hey, Mister Tambourine Man, play a song for me ...

4.   Then take me disappearin' through the smoke rings of my mind
     down the foggy ruins of time, far past the frozen leaves,
     the haunted frightened trees, out to the windy beach,
     far from the twisted reach of crazy sorrow.
     Yes, to dance beneath the diamond sky
     with one hand wavin' free,
     silhouetted by the sea, circled by the circus sands,
     with all memory and fate, driven deep beneath the waves,
     let me forget about today until tomorrow.

Ref.: Hey, Mister Tambourine Man, play a song for me ...

MRS. ROBINSON

♩ 92 | Beat

Words & Music by Paul Simon
© 1968 Paul Simon
All Rights Reserved. International Copyright Secured.

Ref.:
           G   Em

Ref.: And here's to you, Mrs. Robinson,
      G   Em   C   D7
Jesus loves you more than you will know, wo wo wo.
                  G   Em
God bless you, please, Mrs. Robinson,
    G   Em   C   Am   E
heaven holds a place for those who pray, hey, hey, hey, hey, hey, hey.

          E7
1.   We'd like to know a little bit about you for our files,
         A7
     we'd like to help you learn to help yourself.
  D7   G   C   Am
     Look around you, all you see are sympathetic eyes.
  E   D7
     Stroll around the grounds until you feel at home.

              G   Em
Ref.: And here's to you, Mrs. Robinson ...

  E7
2.   Hide in a Hiding Place where no-one ever goes,
     A7
     put in your pantry with your cupcakes.
  D7   G   C   Am
     It's a little secret, just the Robinson's affair.
  E   D7
     Most of all you've got to hide it from the kids.

              G   Em
Ref.: Coo, coo cachoo, Mrs. Robinson ...

  E7
3.   Sitting on a sofa on a Sunday afternoon,
     A7
     going to the candidates' debate.
  D7   G   C   Am
     Laugh about it, shout about it, when you've got to choose.
  E   D7
     Ev'ry way you look at it, you lose.

              G   Em
Ref.: Where have you gone, Joe Dimaggio?
         G   Em   C   D7
     A nation turns its lonely eyes to you, woo woo woo.
              G   Em
     What's that you say, Mrs. Robinson,
         G   Em   C   Am   E
     „Joltin' Joe" has left and gone away, hey, hey, hey, hey, hey, hey.

MY OH MY

♩ 68 | Slow Rock

I be-lieve in wo-man, my oh my.____ I be-lieve
in lov-in', my oh my.____ Don't a wo-man need a man, try and
catch me if you can. I be-lieve in wo-man, my oh my.____ We all
my.____ (instr.)
So let's
my. Yeah, let's all pull to-geth-er, my oh my.____

Words & Music by James Lea & Neville Holder
© by BARN PUBLISHING (SLADE) Ltd.
für Deutschland, GUS und osteuropäische Länder: MUSIKVERLAG INTERSONG GMBH, Hamburg

```
          C        F            C    Em   Am        C
1.   I believe in woman, my oh my. I believe in lovin', my oh my.
          F           C           Dm            F
     Don't a woman need a man, try and catch me, if you can.
     G  C    Dm       F     C G
     I believe in woman, my oh my.

               C              F           C
2.   We all need someone to talk to, my oh my.
              Em          Am          C
     We all need someone to talk to, my oh my.
              F           C         Dm              F
     You need a shoulder to cry on. Call me, I'll be standing by.
     G    C       Dm      F     C G
     We all need someone to talk to, my oh my.
```

```
            C           F           C
3.  We all need a lotta lovin', my oh my.
              Em          Am          C
    Yeah, a whole lotta lovin', my oh my.
          F           C           Dm              F
    I can lend a helping hand, if you ain't got nothing planned.
        G     C       Dm      F      C E
    We all need some lovin', my oh my.
```

A D A C#m F#m E D A Bm D E A Bm7 D A F
(instrumental)

```
        G     C         F           C
4.  So let's all swing together, my oh my.
              Em      Am          C
    We can swing together, my oh my.
                F           C           Dm              F
    You've got troubles of your own, no need to face them all alone.
        G     C       Dm      F     C G
    We can all swing together, my oh my.

        G     C       F           C
5.  So let's all pull together, my oh my.
              Em          Am          C
    Yeah, let's all pull together, my oh my.
                F           C           Dm              F
    We can ride the stormy weather, if we all get out and try,
        G     C       Dm      F     C F
    so let's all pull together, my oh my.
                    C           Dm7     F       C
    Yeah, let's all pull together, my oh my.
```

Words & Music by Vincent Ford
© 1974 Bob Marley Music Ltd. / Blue Mountain Music Ltd., 8 Kensington Park Road, London W11
All Rights Reserved. International Copyright Secured.

```
A    E       F#m D A    D       A E
No woman, no cry.    No woman, no cry.
A    E    F#m A    D       A E
No woman, no cry. No woman, no cry.
A         E    F#m           D
Said I remember when we used to sit
A              E            F#m
in the government yard in Trenchtown.
A         E      F#m
Oberoberserving the hypocrites,
D      A          E           F#m D
as they   mingle with the good people we meet.
A         E       F#m               D
Good friends we have,    good friends we've lost
A E      F#m D A        E
along the way    in this great future.
     F#m         D  A        E    F#m D
You can't forget the past,  so dry your tears, I say.

No woman, no cry ... in the government yard in Trenchtown.
A          E       F#m         D
and then Georgie would make the fire light
A              E            F#m D
as it was log wood burning through the night,
A         E        F#m D    A       E     F#m D
then we would cook corn meal porridge,  of which I'll share with you.
A         E       F#m D    A    E       F#m
I said my feet is my only carriage. So I've got to push on through.
     D
But while I'm gone, I mean:
A          E    F#m                 D E
‖: Ev'rything's gonna be alright.   Ev'rything's gonna be alright.:‖  (4x)
     A E      F#m D A    D       A E
No woman, no cry.    No woman, no cry.
A              E     F#m              D
Woman, little sister, I beg don't shed no tears.
A    D      A E A    E      F#m D
No woman, no cry.    No woman, no cry. (repeat and fade out)
```

145

OB-LA-DI, OB-LA-DA

Words & Music by John Lennon & Paul McCartney

        D   A7

1.   Desmond has a barrow in the market place,

                          D

     Molly is a singer in the band.

     D7   G

     Desmond says to Molly: "Girl, I like your face!"

                 D   A7   D

     and Molly says this, as she takes him by the hand:

                                 F#m Bm D   A7   D

Ref.: " Ob-la-di, ob-la-da, life goes on, bra- la-la how the life goes on.

                                 F#m Bm D   A7   D

    Ob-la-di, ob-la-da, life goes on, bra- la-la how the life goes on."

        D   A7

2.   Desmond takes a trolley to the jeweller's store,

                          D

     buys a twenty carat golden ring.

     D7   G

     Takes it back to Molley, waiting at the door,

                 D   A7   D

     and as he gives it to her, she begins to sing:

                                 F#m

Ref.: " Ob-la-di, ob-la-da, life goes on ...

   G   D

Zw.: In a couple of years they have built a home, sweet home.

   G   D   A7

     With a couple of kids running in the yard of Desmond an Molly Jones.

        D   A7

3.   Happy ever after in the market place,

                            D

     Desmond lets the children lend a hand.

     D7   G

     Molly stays at home and does her pretty face,

               D   A7   D

     and in the evening she's a singer with the band.

                                F#m

Ref.: " Ob-la-di, ob-la-da, life goes on ...

        D   A7

4.   Happy ever after in the market place,

                            D

     Molly lets the children lend a hand.

     D7   G

     Desmond stays at home and does his pretty face,

               D   A7   D

     and in the evening she's a singer with the band.

                             F#m Bm D   A7   D

Ref.: " Ob-la-di, ob-la-da, life goes on, bra- la-la how the life goes on.

                               F#m Bm D   A7   Bm

    Ob-la-di, ob-la-da, life goes on, bra- la-la how the life goes on."

                              A7   D

    And if you want some fun, take ob-la-di-bla-da.

RING OF FIRE

♩ 206 Beat

Words & Music by Merle Kligore & June Carter

```
       C       F       C F C                    G7  C F C
1.    Love is a burning thing    and it makes a fiery ring.
                  F       C F C              G7    C
      Bound by the wild desire,    I fell into a ring of fire.

      G7 C    F              C
Ref.: I fell into a burning ring of fire.
           G7           C          F          C
      I went down, down, down and the flames went higher
                   G  F             C F        C      G7   C
      and it burns, burns, burns, the ring of fire, the ring of fire, the ring of fire.

       C       F       C F C                    G7  C F C
2.    The taste of love is sweet    when hearts like ours beat.
                  F      C F C             G7        C
      I fell for you like a child,    oh, but the fire went wild.
```

I fell into a burning ring of fire ... *(repeat and fade out ad lib.)*

148

SAILING

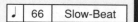

♩ 66 Slow-Beat

I am sail - ing, I am sail - ing, home a-
gain,_____ 'cross the sea. I am sail - ing stor-my
wa - ters to be near you, to be free. free.

Words & Music by Garvin Sutherland
© Universal/Island Music Ltd.

```
         C         Am        F          C
1. I am sailing, I am sailing, home again, 'cross the sea.
         D         Am        Dm         C G7
   I am sailing stormy waters to be near you, to be free.

         C         Am        F          C
2. I am flying, I am flying, like a bird, 'cross the sky.
         D         Am        Dm         C G7
   I am flying passing high clouds to be with you, to be free.

         C           Am              F              C
3. Can you hear me, can you hear me, through the dark night, far away.
         D         Am      Dm        C G7
   I am dying, forever trying to be with you, who can say.

         C         Am        F          C
4. We are sailing, we are sailing, home again, 'cross the sea.
         D         Am        Dm         C
   We are sailing stormy waters to be near you, to be free.
```

RUNAWAY TRAIN

♩ 116 | Medium Beat

C   **G7**   **C**

C   **Em**

Call you up in the midd-le of the night, like a fi-re fly with-

Am

out a light.___ You were there like a blow - torch burn - ing.

F   **G**   𝄋 **C**

I was a key that could use a lit-tle turn-ing.___ So tired that I

Em

could-n't e-ven sleep. So man-y se-crets I could-n't keep.___

Am   **F**

Pro-mised my-self I would-n't weep. One more prom-ise

G   **F**   **G**

I could-n't keep.__ It seems__ no one__ can help__ me now.__ I'm in__

C   **Am**   **F**

too deep,__ there's no__ way__ out.__ This__ time I__ have real-

Em   **G**   ⊕ **C** Refrain

ly led__ my-self___ a-stray.___ Run - a - way train

Em

nev-er go-ing back, wrong way on a one - way track.___

Am   **F**

Seems like I should be get - ting some - where. Some - how I'm nei-ther

1. G   **2. G**   𝄋

here nor there._____ here nor there._____ D.S. al ⊕-⊕

150

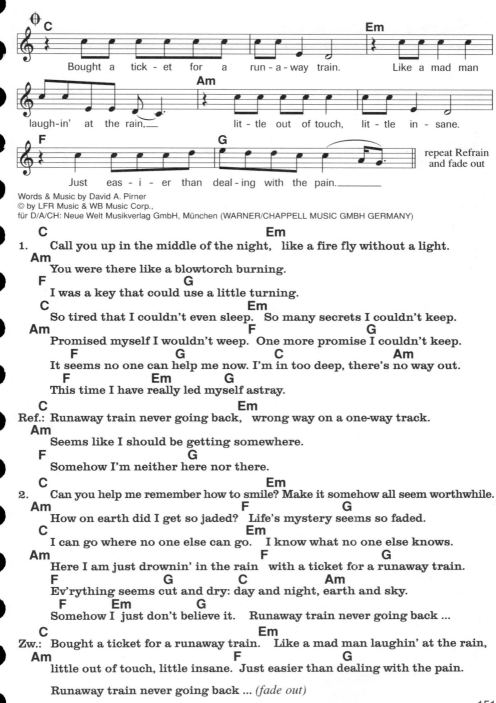

Bought a tick-et for a run-a-way train. Like a mad man

laugh-in' at the rain,___ lit-tle out of touch, lit-tle in-sane.

Just eas-i-er than deal-ing with the pain.___

repeat Refrain
and fade out

Words & Music by David A. Pirner
© by LFR Music & WB Music Corp.,
für D/A/CH: Neue Welt Musikverlag GmbH, München (WARNER/CHAPPELL MUSIC GMBH GERMANY)

      C   Em
1.   Call you up in the middle of the night,   like a fire fly without a light.
  Am
      You were there like a blowtorch burning.
  F   G
      I was a key that could use a little turning.
  C   Em
      So tired that I couldn't even sleep.   So many secrets I couldn't keep.
  Am   F   G
      Promised myself I wouldn't weep. One more promise I couldn't keep.
       F   G   C   Am
      It seems no one can help me now. I'm in too deep, there's no way out.
       F   Em   G
      This time I have really led myself astray.
    C   Em
Ref.: Runaway train never going back,   wrong way on a one-way track.
   Am
      Seems like I should be getting somewhere.
  F   G
      Somehow I'm neither here nor there.
  C   Em
2.   Can you help me remember how to smile? Make it somehow all seem worthwhile.
  Am   F   G
      How on earth did I get so jaded?   Life's mystery seems so faded.
  C   Em
      I can go where no one else can go.   I know what no one else knows.
  Am   F   G
      Here I am just drownin' in the rain   with a ticket for a runaway train.
      F   G   C   Am
      Ev'rything seems cut and dry: day and night, earth and sky.
       F   Em   G
      Somehow I just don't believe it.   Runaway train never going back ...
  C   Em
Zw.: Bought a ticket for a runaway train.   Like a mad man laughin' at the rain,
  Am   F   G
      little out of touch, little insane. Just easier than dealing with the pain.

      Runaway train never going back ... *(fade out)*

SAN FRANCISCO

♩ 120 | Medium-Beat

Bm   **G**   **D**   **A**

(p)
1. If you're go - in'___ to San Fran - cis - co,___
2. For those who come ...

Bm   **G**   **D**   **A**   **Bm**

be sure to wear some flow-ers in your hair.___ If you're

D7   **G**   **D**

go - in'___ to San Fran - cis - co you're gon - na

F#m   **Bm7**   **A**

meet some gen - tle peo - ple there.___

C

All a-cross the na - tion,___ such a strong vi - bra - tion,___

D   **C**

peo-ple in mo - tion.___ There's a whole gen - er - a -

D

tion___ with a new ex - pla - na - tion,___ peo-ple in mo -

A

tion,___ peo - ple in mo - tion.___ D.C. al ⊕-⊕

D   **Bm** **C#m7**   **E**   **A**   **E**

there.___ If you come to San Fran - cis-co,___

G#m   **C#m7**   **E**

sum-mer___ time___ wil be a lov-in___ there.___

A   **E**

___ *(instr.)*

Words & Music by John Phillips
© 1967, 1970 MCA Music (a division of MCA Incorporated), USA
Universal/MCA Music Ltd., 77 Fulham Palace Road, London W6 for the world (excluding North, Central & South America, Japan, Australasia and the Philippines). All Rights Reserved. International Copyright Secured.

```
    Bm          G      D       A
1.    If you're goin' to San Francisco,
    Bm          G          D            A
      be sure you wear some flowers in your hair.
    Bm          D7     G        D
      If you're goin' to San Francisco,
                    F#m        Bm7          A
      you're gonna meet some gentle people there.


    Bm              G        D      A
2.    For those who come to San Francisco,
    Bm       G       D          A
      summertime will be a lovin' there.
    Bm       D7       G        D
      In the streets of  San Francisco,
                F#m          Bm7          A
      gentle people with flowers in their hair.


    C
      All across the nation such a strong vibration,
    D
      people in motion.
    C
      There's a whole generation with a new explanation,
    D                  A
      people in motion,   people in motion.


    Bm              G        D      A
3.    For those who come to San Francisco,
    Bm       G       D              A
      be sure to wear some flowers in your hair.
    Bm     D7    G      D
      If you come to San Francisco,
              F#m      Bm7        D    Bm
      summertime will be a lovin' there.


C#m7        E       A       E
      If you come to San Francisco,
                G#m      C#m7        E
      summertime will be a lovin' there.
```

SHAPE OF MY HEART

♩ 96 | Medium Beat

Mm._____ Yeah, yeah. Ba - by,__ please__ try__ to for - give__ me.__ Stay__ here,__ don't put out the__ glow._____ Hold me now, don't both - er if ev'ry min - ute it makes me weak - er. You__ can__ save__ me__ from the man that I've__ be - come._____ Oh, yeah.__ Look - ing__ back on the things__ I've__ done,_____ I__ was__ try - ing to be__ some - one. I played__ my__ part_____ and kept you in the dark. Now let me show__ you__ the__ shape__ of_____ my heart.__ shape__ of_____ my heart. __ I'm__ here with my con - fes - sion._____ Got no - thing to hide no__ more.__ I don't know where__ to__ start_____ but to show you_____ the__ shape of_____ my heart.__ I'm look - ing back

154

on things I've done. I never wanna play the same old part and keep you in the dark. Now let me show you the shape of my heart. The things I've done, I was trying to be some-one. I played my part and kept you in the dark. Now let me show you the shape of my heart.

shape of, show you the shape of my heart.

Words & Music by Martin Sandberg, Rami Yacoub & Lisa Miskovsky
© 2000 Grantsville Publishing Ltd. SVL: Musikedition Discoton GmbH (BMG Musikverlage) München
Für D/A/CH, GUS, Rumänien, Bulgarien, Albanien, ehem. Jugoslawien
Universal Music Publishing Limited, 77 Fulham Palace Road, London W6. All Rights Reserved. International Copyright Secured

           C   G   F G7 C   G   F G7

1.   Baby, please try to forgive me.   Stay here, don't put out the glow.

           C   G

Hold me now, don't bother if ev'ry minute it takes me weaker.

     F   C   D   F

You can save me from the man that I've become. Oh yeah.

                C   F   C   G

Ref.: Looking back on the things I've done, I was trying to be someone.

  Em   Am   D

I played my part and kept you in the dark.

              F   G   F

Now let me show you the shape of my heart.

           C   G   F

2.   Sadness is beautiful, loneliness is tragical.

    G7 C   G F G7

So help me, I can't win this wa r, oh no.

      C   G

Touch me now, don't bother if ev'ry second it takes me weaker.

     F   C   D

You can save me from the man that I've become.

```
             G7      C                      F   C      G
Ref.: Looking back on the things I've done, I was trying to be someone.
      Em           Am                    D
      I played my part and kept you in the dark.
                   F            E   E7    Am
      Now let me show you the shape of my heart.


            G        C     F    Am   G        C    F
      I'm here with my confession.   Got nothing to hide  no more.
              Dm           E          F        E   Am G   C
      I don't know where to start, but to show you the shape of  my heart.
      D          G        D
      I'm looking back on things I've done.
      A        F#m            Bm              E
      I never wanna play the same old part and keep you in the dark.
      A7   G               A         D
      Now let me show you the shape of my heart.
                  G   D      A
      The things I've done, I was trying to be someone.
      F#m        Bm                     E
      I played my part and kept you in the dark.
                  A7  G       D   A
      Now let me show you the shape of my heart.
                  G   D      A
      The things I've done, I was trying to be someone.
      F#m        Bm                     E
      I played my part and kept you in the dark.
                  A7  G       D   A   G          D   A      D
      Now let me show you the shape of, show you the shape of  my heart.
```

SOUND OF SILENCE

| ♩ | 102 | Beat |

```
   Am                          G                        Am
1.    Hello darkness, my old friend, I've come to talk to you again,
           C      F     C                       F      C
      because a vision softly creeping left its seeds, while I was sleeping
           F                         C
      and the vision that was planted in my brain
       Em    Am C        G       Am
      still remains   within the sound of silence.

   Am                             G                        Am
2.    In restless dreams I walked alone narrow streets of cobblestone.
           C      F     C                           F         C
      'Neath the halo of a street lamp I turned my collar to the cold and damp.
           F                             C
      When my eyes were stabbed by the flash of a neon light
       Em    Am C        G      Am
      that split the night   and touched the sound of silence.
```

Am   G   Am

3. And in the naked light I saw ten thousand people, maybe more,

         C   F   C   F   C

    people talking without speaking, people hearing without listening,

                       F   C

    people writing songs that voices never share

        Em   Am C   G   Am

    and no one dare   disturb the sound of silence.

Am   G   Am

4. Fools, said I, ain't you not know, silence like a cancer grows.

         C   F   C   F   C

    Hear my words that I might teach you, take my arms that I might reach you.

                F   C

    But my words like silent raindrops fell

Am   G   Am

    and echoed in the wells of silence.

Am   G   Am

5. And the people bowed and prayed to the neon god they made.

         C   F   C   F   C

    And the sign flashed out its warning in the words that it was forming.

                       F   C

    And the sign said: "The words of the prophets are written on the subway walls

        Em   Am   C   G   Am

    and tenement halls and whisper in the sound of silence.

Hel-lo darkness, my old friend, I've come to talk to you a-gain, be-cause a vi-sion soft-ly creep-ing left its seeds while I was sleep-ing and the vi-sion that was plan-ted in my brain still re-mains with-in the sound of si-lence.

4x D.S.

Words & Music by Paul Simon
© 1964 Paul Simon

Am   F   Dm

one,   yes, she's the one.___   If there's some-bo   -   dy   call-ing me on,___

G   Am   B♭

___   she's the one,___   she's the one.___   If   there's some - bo -

Dm   G   C   F   C   F   C

dy   call-ing me on,___   she's the one,___   She's the one.

Words & Music by Karl Wallinger
© 1996 PolyGram Music Publishing Limited
Universal Music Publishing Limited, 77 Fulham Palace Road, London W6
All Rights Reserved. International Copyright Secured.

         C   F   C   F
1.   I was her, she was me, we were one, we were free.
           Dm   G7   C
     And if there's somebody calling me on, she's the one.
F   Dm   G   C
     If there's somebody calling me on, she's the one.

         C   F   C   F
2.   We were young, we were wrong, we were fine all along.
           Dm   G7   C   B♭ C7
     If there's somebody calling me on, she's the one.

   F
Zw.:   When you get to where you wanna go
                                  C   B♭   C
     and you know the things you wanna know, you're   smiling.
   F
     When you said what you wanna say
     and you know the way you wanna play, yeah.
Dm   Dm7 G
     You'll be so high you'll be fly - ing.

         C   F   C   F
3.   Though the sea will be strong I know we'll carry on.
           Dm   G7   C
     'Cos if there's somebody calling me on, she's the one.
F   Dm   G   C
     If there's somebody calling me on, she's the one.

         C   F   C   F   C
4.   I was her, she was me, we were one, we were free ... she's the one.
F   Dm   G   C
     If there's somebody calling me on, she's the one.
C7   Dm   G   Am   F
     If there's somebody calling me on, she's the one, yes she's the one.
             Dm   G   Am   B♭
‖: If there's somebody calling me on, she's the one, she's the one. :‖
            Dm   G   C   F C F   C
     If there's somebody calling me on, she's the one.   She's the one.

159

SPIRIT OF THE HAWK

♩ | 118 | Disco-Beat

A - He, A - He, A - He Ya-ma-ma he-ya-mama

he-ya-ma-ma Ja-he-ya-ma-ya o-ma-hey The Spi-rit of the hawk.

___ He-ya-ma he-ya-ma-ma he-ya-ma-ma Ja-he-ya-ma-ma o-ma-

hey. The spi-rit of_ the hawk. hey. He am my he - ro,___

he am my love._ High on a hill - side,___

hea-ven a-bove._ Drift-ing through high_ and low,___

we fly a-way._ Me and my he - ro,___ me and my love.

The spi-rit of_ the hawk._ He-ya-ma he-ya-ma-ma he-ya-ma-ma Ja -

he-ya ma-ya o-ma - hey. The spi-rit of_ the hawk. hey. *(instr.)*

D.S.
(con rep.)
al ⊕-⊕

hey. The spi-rit of_ the hawk. He-ya-ma he-ya-ma-ma he-ya-ma-ma Ja -

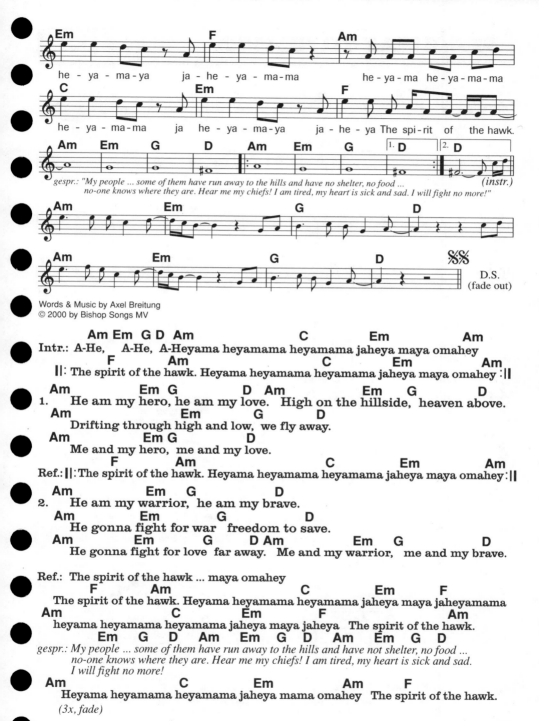

he - ya - ma - ya   ja - he - ya - ma - ma   he - ya - ma he - ya - ma - ma

he - ya - ma - ma   ja he - ya - ma - ya   ja - he - ya The spi - rit of the hawk.

gespr.: "My people ... some of them have run away to the hills and have no shelter, no food ...
no-one knows where they are. Hear me my chiefs! I am tired, my heart is sick and sad. I will fight no more!"   *(instr.)*

D.S.
(fade out)

Words & Music by Axel Breitung

      Am Em G D Am   C   Em   Am
Intr.: A-He,   A-He, A-Heyama heyamama heyamama jaheya maya omahey
            F   Am   C   Em   Am
‖: The spirit of the hawk. Heyama heyamama heyamama jaheya maya omahey :‖

   Am   Em G   D Am   Em   G   D
1.   He am my hero, he am my love.   High on the hillside, heaven above.
   Am   Em   G   D
      Drifting through high and low, we fly away.
   Am   Em G   D
      Me and my hero, me and my love.
            F   Am   C   Em   Am
Ref.: ‖: The spirit of the hawk. Heyama heyamama heyamama jaheya maya omahey :‖

   Am   Em G   D
2.   He am my warrior, he am my brave.
   Am   Em   G   D
      He gonna fight for war   freedom to save.
   Am   Em   G   D Am   Em G   D
      He gonna fight for love far away.   Me and my warrior,   me and my brave.

Ref.: The spirit of the hawk ... maya omahey
            F   Am   C   Em   F
   The spirit of the hawk. Heyama heyamama heyamama jaheya maya jaheyamama
Am   C   Em   F   Am
   heyama heyamama heyamama jaheya maya jaheya The spirit of the hawk.
            Em G D Am Em G D Am Em G D
gespr.: My people ... some of them have run away to the hills and have not shelter, no food ...
no-one knows where they are. Hear me my chiefs! I am tired, my heart is sick and sad.
I will fight no more!
Am   C   Em   Am   F
   Heyama heyamama heyamama jaheya mama omahey The spirit of the hawk.
   (3x, fade)

161

STAIRWAY TO HEAVEN

72-98 | Rock

(langsam beginnen, Tempo kontinuierlich steigern)

Am ... E ... C ... D
There's a la - dy who's shure all that glit - ters is gold__ and she's

F ... G Am ... E
buy - ing a stair - way__ to hea - ven. When she gets there she knows if the

C ... D ... F ... 1.G Am ... C ... D
stores are all closed with a word she can get what she came for.__ Ooh,__

F ... Am ... C ... G ... D
ooh,__ and she's buy - ing a stair - way to hea - ven. There's a

2.G Am ... E C D ... F G Am G Am ... D
giv - en. Ooh, it makes me

Am ... Em ... D ... C D ... Am ... D
won - der.__ Ooh__ it makes me won - der.

Am Em ... D ... C D ... C ... G ... Am
There's a feel - ing I get when I look to the west, and my

C ... G ... F ... Am ... C ... G
spir - it is cry-ing for leav - ing.__ In my thoughts I have seen rings of

Am ... C ... G ... F
smoke through the trees and the voic - es of those who stand look -

Am ... 1.C G Am ... 2.C G Am ... D ... Am Em D ... C D
ing.__

C ... G ... Am
If there's a bus - tle in your hedge-row,__ don't be a-larmed now,

162

Words & Music by Jimmy Page / Robert Plant
© Superhype Publishing. Für Deutschland, Schweiz, osteuropäische Staaten (ohne Baltikum), Türkei und Länder des ehem.
Jugoslawien: NEUE WELT MUSIKVERLAG GMBH

```
           Am        E        C       D
There's a lady who's sure all that glitters is gold
           F                  G Am
and she's buying a stairway to heaven.
                 E              C              D
When she gets there, she knows, if the stores are all closed
          F                   G    Am
with a word she can get what she came for.
C   D   F Am        C        G        D
Ooh, ooh,   and she's buying a stairway to heaven.
            C          D           F          Am
There's a sign on the wall, but she wants to be sure
          C              D          F
'cause you know sometimes words have two meanings.
      Am        E           C          D
In a tree by the brook there's a song bird who sings,
           F                         G Am E C D F G Am G Am
sometimes all of our thoughts are misgiven.
D               Am Em D C D Am D                  Am Em D C
Ooh, it makes me wonder.      Ooh,  it makes me wonder.
      D      C      G        Am
There's a feeling I get, when I look to the west,
          C       G       F Am
and my spirit is crying for leaving.
            C          G            Am
I my thoughts I have seen, rings of smoke through the trees
          C       G          F Am   C G Am
and the voices of those who stand looking.
 D                     Am Em D C D
Ooh, it makes me wonder.
Am  D                      Am Em D C D
Ooh,   it really makes me wonder.
            C           G       Am
And it's whispered that soon, if we all call the tune,
            C       G        F Am
then the piper will lead us to reason.
            C      G        Am
And a new day will dawn for those who stand long
            C       G       F   Am  C G Am D Am Em D C D
and the forests will echo with laughter.
C         G          Am
If there's a bustle in your hedgerow, don't be alarmed now,
C         G                 F Am
it's just a spring clean for the May queen.
C         G              Am
Yes, there are two paths you can go by, but in the long run
C         G              F      Am C G Am
there's still time to change the road you're on.
D                 Am   Em D C D Am D Am Em D C D
And it makes me wonder.
C         G            Am
Your head is humming and it won't go in case you don't know,
C         G            F Am
the piper's calling you to join him.
C         G            Am
Dear lady can you hear the wind blow, and did you know
```

```
      C                    G              F    Am        C G D
   your stairway lies on the whispering wind.
Am            G                    F  G Am          G              F  G
   And as we wind on down the road,      our shadows taller than our soul,
Am            G          F  G Am              G                    F
   there walks a lady we all know    who shines white light and wants to show
Am        G              F  G
   how ev'rything still turns to gold.
Am          G          F  G Am            G              F
   And if you listen very hard,      the tune will come to you at last.
Am            G          F Am      G        Am
   When all are one and one is all,   to be a rock not to roll.
   F                        G Am
   And she's buying a stairway to heaven.
```

SUPER TROUPER

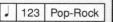

♩ 123 | Pop-Rock

Su - per trou - per beams are gon-na blind me but I won't feel blue

like I al-ways do 'cause somewhere in the crowd there's you.

I was sick and tired of ev'-ry-

thing when I called you last night from Glas - gow. All I do is eat and sleep and

sing, wish-ing ev' - ry show was the last show. So i - ma-gine I was

glad to hear you're com-ing, sud-den-ly I feel al - right and it's gon-na be so

diff'-rent when I'm on the stage to - night. To-night the su - per trou-per

lights are gon-na find__ me, shin - ing like the sun, smi-ling, hav - ing

fun, feel-ing like a num - ber one. To-night the su - per trou-per

beams are gon-na blind me but I won't feel blue like I al-ways do 'cause

1. somewhere in the crowd there's 2. somewhere in the crowd there's you.

So I'll be there when you ar-rive, the sight of you will prove to me I'm still a-live and when you take me in your arms and hold me tight, I know it's gon-na mean so much to - night. To-night the su - per trou - per lights are gon-na find__ me, shin - ing like the sun, smi - ling, hav - ing fun, feel - ing like a num - ber one.

Words & Music by Benny Andersson & Björn Ulvaeus
© 1980 Union Songs AB, Stockholm, Sweden for the world.
Universal Music Publ. GmbH
All Rights Reserved. International Copyright Secured.

       C   G7

Intr.: Super trouper beams are gonna blind me, but I won't feel blue
      Dm   G   G7   C

like I always do, 'cause somewhere in the crowd there's you.

       C   Em   Dm   G7

1.   I was sick and tired of ev'rything, when I called you last night from Glasgow.
       C   Em   Dm   G7

    All I do is eat and sleep and sing, wishing ev'ry show was the last show.
    F   C   F   C

    So imagine I was glad to hear you're coming, suddenly I feel alright
    F   C   G7

    and it's gonna be so diff'rent, when I'm on the stage tonight.

                            C   G7

Ref.: Tonight the super trouper beams are gonna find me, shining like the sun,
      Dm   G   G7   C

    smiling, having fun, feeling like a number one.
                            C   G7

    Tonight the super trouper beams are gonna blind me, but I won't feel blue
    Dm   G   G7   C

    like I always do, 'cause somewhere in the crowd there's you.

       C   Em   Dm   G7

2.   Facing twenty thousand of your friends, how can anyone be so lonely.
       C   Em   Dm   G7

    Part of our success that never ends, still I'm thinking about you only.
    F   C   F   C

    There are moments, when I think I'm going crazy, but it's gonna be alright.
    F   C   G7

    ev'rything will be so diff'rent, when I'm on the stage tonight.

Ref.: Tonight the super trouper ... 'cause somewhere in the crowd there's you.

             F   Am
Zw.: So I'll be there, when you arrive,

           Dm   G   C
the sight of you will prove to me I'm still alive,

                          F   Dm A7
and when you take me in your arms and hold me tight,

  Dm   G
I know it's gonna mean so much tonight.

Ref.: Tonight the super trouper ... 'cause somewhere in the crowd there's you.

            C   G7
Tonight the super trouper beams are gonna find me, shining like the sun,

  Dm   G G7   C
smiling, having fun, feeling like a number one.

THROUGH THE BARRICADES   ♩ | 72 | Slow-Beat

     D   Bm   F#m7
1.   Mother doesn't know where love has gone,

   G   Bm   C   G
she says it must be youth that keeps us feeling strong.

   D   Bm   F#m7
See it in her face that's turned to ice,

   G   Bm   G   A
and when she smiles, she shows the lines of sacrifice.

                  G   A   D D/C# Bm
Ref.: And now I know what they're saying as our sun begins to fade.

             G   Em   A   D
And we made our love on waste land and through the barricades.

```
      D          Bm          F#m7
2.    Father  made my history
      G             Bm                    C              G
      he fought for what he thought would set us somehow free.
      D                    Bm              F#m7
      They taught me what to say in school,
      G          Bm             G              A
      I learned it off by heart, but now that's torn in two.

                     G           A            C    G D
Ref.: And now I know ... and through the barricades.

      D          Bm          F#m7
3.    Born on different sides of life
      G          Bm           C            G
      but we feel the same and feel all of this strive,
      D             Bm              F#m7
      so come to me, when I'm asleep
      G          Bm             G              A
      and we'll cross the line and dance upon the streets.

                     G           A            D
Ref.: And now I know ... and through the barricades.

      C    G                   D             C              G
Zw.:  Oh, turn around and I'll be there, there's a scar right through my heart,
                      D
      but I'll bear it again.
                 C                 G
      Oh, I thought we were the human race,
                     D           D/C#      Bm
      but we were just another borderline case.
                     G                                              A
      And the stars reach down and tell us that there's always one escape.

      D           A          Bm
4.    Oh I don't know where love has gone,
      G                  Bm         G              A
      and in this troubled  land desperation keeps us strong.
      D           A          Bm
      Friday's child is full of soul
      G           Bm              G              A
      with nothing left to lose there's ev'rything to go.

                     G               A           D    D/C#       Bm
Ref.: And now I know what they're saying, it's a terrible beauty we've made.
      A     G                E                A              D
      so we make our love on waste land and through the barricades.
               A  G           A           Bm   A     G
      And now I know what they're saying as our hearts go to their graves,
                         Em  G           A                   C G
      so we made our love on waste land and through the barricades. (fade out)
```

169

Moth-er does-n't know where love has gone,___ she says it must___ be youth___ that keeps us feel - ing strong.

See it in her face that's turned to ice, and when she smiles, she shows the lines___ of___ sa-cri - fice.

And now I___ know what they're say - ing as our sun be-gins___ to fade. And we made___ our love on waste land___ and through the bar - ri - cades.

cades.

cades. Oh, turn a-round___ and I'll be there, there's a scar right through my heart,___ but I'll bear it a - gain.

Oh, I thought we were the hu - man race___ but we were just an - oth - er bor - der - line___ case. And the stars___

reach down and tell us that there's al - ways one es-cape.

Oh,_____ I don't know where love has gone,

and in this trou-bled land des - per - a - tion keeps us

strong.__ Fri - day's child__ is full of soul__

with noth-ing__ left__ to lose there's ev' - ry-thing to go.

D.S. al

cades. And now I know what they're say - ing as our hearts

go__ to their__ graves, so we made our love on waste_____

land__ and__ through the bar - ri-cades.

(fade out)

Words & Music by Gary Kemp
© Reformation Music Publ. Co. Ltd.
für Deutschland, Österreich, Schweiz und Ost-Europa: Edition Intro Meisel GmbH

SURFIN' U.S.A.

♩ 160 | Rock 'n' Roll

If ev'-ry-bod-y had an o-cean a-cross the U. S. A.,___ then ev'-ry-bod-y'd be surf-in'___ like Cal-i-for-ni-a.___ You see them wear-in' their bag-gies,___ Huar-a-chi san-dals, too.___ A bush-y bush-y blond hair-do,___ surf-in' U. S. A.___ You'll catch 'em surf-in' at Del Mar,___ Ven-tu-ra Coun-try Line,___ San-ta Cruz and Tress-els,___ Aus-tra-lia's Nar-a-bine.___ All o-ver Man-hat-tan___ and down Do-he-ny way.___ Ev'-ry-bod-y's gone surf-in',___ surf-in' U. S. A.___ We'll all be plan'-in' out a surf-in' U. S. A.___

Ev'-ry-bod-y's gone

surf - in',___   surf-in' U. S. A.___   Ev' - ry - bod-y's gone

(fade out)

Words by Brian Wilson, Music by Chuck Berry
© 1958, 1963 by Arc Music Corp., New York
Good Tunes Music AG, Genf, für Deutschland, Österreich und Schweiz

                      G7   **C**
1.   If ev'rybody had an ocean across the U.S.A,
                           G7   **C**
    then ev'rybody'd be surfin' like California.
C7   **F**   **C**
    You see them wearin' their baggies, Huarachi sandals, too.
                       G7 F   **C**
    A bushy, bushy blond hairdo, surfin' U.S.A.

                       G7   **C**
2.   You'll catch 'em surfin' at Del Mar, Ventura Country Line,
                     G7   **C**
    Santa Cruz and Tressels, Australia's Narabine.
C7   **F**   **C**
    All over Manhattan and down Doheny way.
                   G7 F   **C**
    Ev'rybody's gone surfin', surfin' U.S.A.

                     G7   **C**
3.   We'll all be planin' out a route, we're gonna take real soon.
                    G7   **C**
    We're waxin' down our surfboards, we can't wait for June.
C7   **F**   **C**
    We'll all be gone for the summer, we're on safari to stay.
                   G7 F   **C**
    Tell the teacher we're surfin', surfin' U.S.A.

                     G7   **C**
4.   At Haggarty's and Swammi's, Pacific Palisades,
                    G7   **C**
    San Onofre and Sunset, Redondo Beach, L.A.
C7   **F**   **C**
    All over La Jolla, at Waiamea Bay,
                   G7 F   **C**
    ev'rybody's gone surfin', surfin' U.S.A.

   G7 C G7 C C7 F C
   (instrumental break)
                   G7 F   **C**
   Ev'rybody's gone surfin', surfin' U.S.A. *(repeat and fade out)*

SWEET HOME ALABAMA

♩ 98 | Country Rock

Big wheels keep on turn-ing, car-ry me home to see my kin. Sing-ing songs a-bout the Southland, I miss Al' - ba-ma once a-gain. —— *(And I think it's a sin, yes)* Sweet home A - la-ba-ma, where the skies are so blue, sweet home A - la-ba-ma, Lord, I'm com-ing home to you. you. *(fade out)*

D.C. al

Words & Music by Ronnie van Zant, Ed King & Gary Rossington
© 1974 MCA Music (a division of MCA Inc., USA) / Universal/MCA Music Ltd., 77 Fulham Palace Road, London W6
All Rights Reserved. International Copyright Secured.

    A   G   D   A   G   D
1. Big wheels keep on turning,   carry me home to see my kin.
    A   G   D   A   G   D
    Singing songs about the Southland,   I miss Al'bama once again.
    (And I think it's a sin, yes)

    A   G   D
2. Well, I heard Mister Young sing about her.
    A   G   D
    Well, I heard ole Neil put her down.
    A   G   D
    Well, I hope Neil Young will remember,
    A   G   D
    a Southern man don't need him around anyhow.

174

```
      A            G        D   G A         G            D
Ref.: Sweet home Alabama,      where the skies are so blue.
      A            G        D   G A         G              D
      Sweet home Alabama,      Lord, I'm coming home to you.

      A                 G              D        C G
3.    In Birmingham they love the gov'nor.
      A                 G              D
      Now we all did what we could do.
      A              G          D
      Now Watergate does not  bother me.
      A                G              D
      Does your conscience bother you?
      (Tell the truth.)

      A                 G                    D
4.    Now Muscle Shoals has got the Swampers
      A                    G                      D
      and they've been known to pick a song or two.
      A              G        D
      Lord they get me off so much,
      A                G                  D
      they pick me up, when I'm feeling blue.
      (Now how about you?)

      A            G        D   G A         G            D
Ref.: Sweet home Alabama,      where the skies are so blue.
      A            G        D   G A         G              D
      Sweet home Alabama,      Lord, I'm coming home to you.
```

TALKIN' BOUT A REVOLUTION

♩ 114 | Rock

Don't you know___ they're talk-in' a-bout a re - vo - lu - tion, it sounds like a

1. whis - per.

2. whis - per. While they're

stand-ing in the wel - fare lines,___ cry-ing at the door-steps of those arm - ies of sal - va - tion, wast - ing time___ in the un-em-ploy - ment lines, sit-ting a - round, wai-ting for a pro - mo - tion.

Don't you know___ they're talk - in' a-bout a re - vo-lu - tion, it sounds___ like a whis-per.

Poor peo-ple gon-na rise up___ and get their___ share.___

Don't you know you'd bet - ter run, run, run, run, run, run, run, run, run, run, run,___ run.___

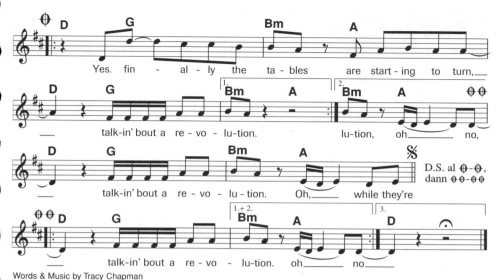

Words & Music by Tracy Chapman
© 1988 Purple Rabbit Music / EMI April Music Inc., USA
EMI Songs Ltd., London WC2H 0QY
Reproduced by permission of IMP Ltd.   All Rights Reserved

D   G   Bm   A   D   G   Bm A

||:Don't you know they're talkin' about a revolution, it sounds like a whisper. :||

D   G   Bm A

While they're standing in the welfare lines,

D   G   Bm   A

crying at the doorsteps of those armies of salvation,

D   G   Bm   A

wasting time in the unemployment lines,

D   G   Bm   A

sitting around, waiting for a promotion.

D   G   Bm   A   D   G   Bm A

Don't you know they're talkin' about a revolution, it sounds like a whisper.

D   G   Bm A   D   G Bm A

Poor people gonna rise up   and get their share

D   G   Bm A   D   G Bm A

poor people gonna rise up   and take what's theirs.

D

||:Don't you know, you'd better run, run, run, run,

Bm   A   D   G Bm A

run, run, run, run, run, run, run, run. :||

D   G   Bm A   D   G   Bm   A

Yes, finally the tables are starting to turn, talkin' bout a revolution.

D   G   Bm A   D   G   Bm   A D

Yes, finally the tables are starting to turn, talkin' bout a revolution, oh no,

G   Bm   A   D

talkin' bout a revolution. Oh, while they're   standing in the welfare lines ...

Bm   A D   G   Bm   G   Bm   A D

... like a whisper.   Yes, finally the tables ... talkin' bout a revolution, oh no,

G   Bm   A D

||: talkin' bout a revolution, oh no, :|| (3x)

THE BOXER

164 | Shuffle

Words & Music by Paul Simon

                    C   Am
1.   I am just a poor boy, though my story's seldom told,
                    G   Dm   G
      I have squandered my resistance for a pocket full of mumbles,
                          C
      such are promises.
                    Am   G   F
      All lies are jest, still a man hears what he wants to hear
                                C   G G7 C
      and disregards the rest. Hm-m Hm-m

                    C   Am
2.   When I left my home and family, I was no more than a boy
                    G   Dm   G
      in the company of strangers in the quiet of the railway-
                    C
      station running scared.
                    Am   G   F
      Laying low, seeking out the poorer quarters where
                                C   G   F   G   C
      the ragged people go, looking for the places only they would know.

                    Am   G   Am
Ref.: Lie la lie, lie la lie la lie la lie, lie la lie,
                    G   F   C
      lie la lie la lie la lie la la la la lie.

                    C   Am
3.   Asking only workman's wages I come looking for a job,
                          G   Dm   G
      but I get no offers, just the „Come on" from the whores on
                    C
      Seventh Avenue.
                    Am   G   F
      I do declare there were times, when I was so lonesome
                                C   G F G   C
      I took some comfort there, la la la, la la la la.   *Refrain*

                    C   Am
4.   Then I'm laying out my winter clothes and wishing I was gone,
                    G   Dm   G
      going home, where the New York City winters
                    C   Em   Am   G   F   C
      aren't bleeding me,   leading me, going home, Hm Hm

                    C   Am
5.   In the clearing stands a boxer and a fighter by his trade,
                    G   Dm   G
      and he carries the reminders of ev'ry glove that laid him
                    C
      down or cut him till he cried out
                                Am   G   F
      in his anger and his shame: „I am leaving, I am leaving!" but
                          C   G F   G   C
      the fighter still remains. Hm Hm Hm Hm

                    Am   G   Am
Ref.: Lie la lie, lie la lie la lie la lie, lie la lie,
                    G   F   C
      lie la lie la lie la lie la la la la lie.

THE TIMES, THEY ARE A-CHANGING

♩ | 171 | Country-Waltz

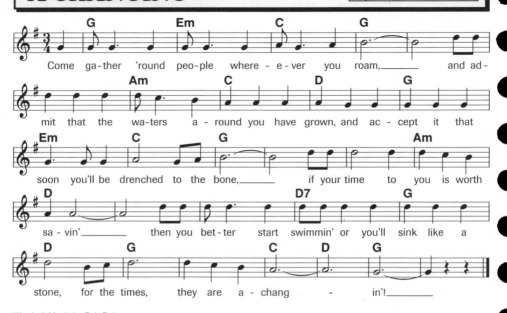

Come ga-ther 'round peo-ple where-e-ver you roam,_____ and ad-mit that the wa-ters a-round you have grown, and ac-cept it that soon you'll be drenched to the bone,_____ if your time to you is worth sa-vin'_____ then you bet-ter start swimmin' or you'll sink like a stone, for the times, they are a-chang - in'!_____

Words & Music by Bob Dylan
© 1963 M. Witmark & Sons, USA
© renewed 1990 Special Rider Music, USA. This arrangement © 2000 Special Rider Music
All Rights Reserved. International Copyright Secured.

1.
```
        G          Em        C          G
Come gather 'round people, wherever you roam,
                Am       C          D
and admit that the waters around you have grown
        G          Em           C           G
and accept it that soon you'll be drenched to the bone,
           Am        D
if your time to you is worth savin',
                    D7              G            D
then you better start swimmin' or you'll sink like a stone,
        G               C D G
for the times, they are a-chan- gin'!
```

2.
```
         G            Em          C                G
Come writers and critics who prophesy with your pen
                  Am          C           D
and keep your eyes wide, the chance won't come again.
        G          Em         C            G
And don't speak too soon, for the wheel's still in spin
                    Am         D
and there's no tellin' who that it's namin'
        D7              G       D         G              C D G
for the loser now will be later to win, for the times, they are a-chan- gin'!
```

```
        G        Em           C          G
3.  Come senators, congressmen, please heed the call
                 Am           C          D
    don't stay in the doorway, don't block up the hall.
        G        Em       C          G
    For he that gets hurt, will be he who has stalled,
                 Am          D
    there's a battle outside and it's ragin',
                         D7        G            D
    it'll soon shake your windows and rattle your walls,
            G               C D G
    for the times, they are a-chan- gin'!

        G        Em           C          G
4.  Come mothers and fathers throughout the land
                 Am           C          D
    and don't criticize what you can't understand.
        G        Em           C              G
    Your sons and your daughters are beyond your command.
                 Am      D
    Your old road is rapidly agin'.
                         D7          G            D
    please get out of the new one, if you can't lend your hand,
            G               C D G
    for the times, they are a-chan- gin'!

        G     Em        C          G
5.  The line it is drawn, the curse, it is cast
                 Am      C      D
    the slow one now will later be fast.
        G     Em    C      G
    As the present now will later be past
                 Am      D
    the order is rapidly fadin'
                     D7      G          D
    and the first one now will later be last,
            G               C D G
    for the times, they are a-chan- gin'!
```

TICKET TO RIDE

♩ | 120 | Beat

Words & Music by John Lennon & Paul McCartney
© 1965 Northern Songs
All Rights Reserved. International Copyright Secured.

182

                    D
1.   I think I'm gonna be sad, I think it's today, yeah!
                                              Em7 A7
     The girl that's driving me mad is going away.
     Bm   **G**   **Bm**   **C**
     She's got a ticket to ride, she's got a ticket to ri-hi-hide,
     Bm   **A7**   **D**
     she's got a ticket to ride, but she don't care.

                    D
2.   She said that living with me is bringing her down, yeah!
                                              Em7 A7
     For she would never be free, when I was around.
     Bm   **G**   **Bm**   **C**
     She's got a ticket to ride, she's got a ticket to ri-hi-hide,
     Bm   **A7**   **D**
     she's got a ticket to ride, but she don't care.

          G7
Zw.: I don't know why she's riding so high.
                                                        A7
     She ought to think right, she ought to do right by me.
          G7
     Before she gets to saying good bye,
                                                   A A7
     she ought to think right, she ought to do right by me.

                    D
3.   She said that living with me is bringing her down, yeah!
                                              Em7 A7
     For she would never be free, when I was around.
     Bm   **G**   **Bm**   **C**
     She's got a ticket to ride, she's got a ticket to ri-hi-hide,
     Bm   **A7**   **D**
     she's got a ticket to ride, but she don't care.

     My baby don't care. My baby don't care ... *(fade out)*

WHAT'S UP

♩ 104 | Medium Beat

Twen-ty-five years and my life is still___ try-ing to get up that

great big hill___ of___ hope___ for a des-ti - na - tion. I

re-al-ised quick - ly as I knew I should that this world was made up of this

bro-ther-hood of___ man___ for what-e - ver that means.

And so I cry some-times when I'm ly - ing in bed___ just to

get it all out___ what's in___ my head.___ And I___ and I'm feel-ing

a lit-tle pe-cu - li-ar.___ And so I wake ev'-ry morning and I

step out - side___ an I take a deep breath and I get___ real high.___ And I

scream from the top of my lungs,___ "What' go - ing on?"___

      G
1.   Twenty-five years and my life is still
      Am   **C**   **G**
      trying to get up that great big hill of hope for a destination.
      G
      I realised quickly, as I knew I should, that this
      Am   **C**   **G**
      world was made up of this brotherhood of man, for whatever that means.

      And so I cry sometimes, when I'm lying in bed
                   Am
      just to get it all out what's in my head.
         C   **G**
      And I - I am feeling a little peculiar.

      And so I wake up ev'ry morning and I step outside
                Am
      and I take a deep breath and I get real high.
         C   **G**
      And I   scream from the top of my lungs, "What's going on?"

                    G   **Am**   **G**
Ref.: And I say: Hey hey hey hey hey hey. I say: "Hey, what's going on?"
                    G   **Am**   **G**
      And I say: Hey hey hey hey hey hey. I say: "Hey, what's going on?"
                Am C
      Uh uh uh   uh

      G
2.   And I try, oh my God, do I
      Am   **C**   **G**
      try, I try all the time in this institution.
             G
      And I pray, oh my God, do I
      Am   **C**   **G**
      pray, I pray ev'ry single day for a revolution.

      And so I cry sometimes when I'm lying in bed ...

                    G   **Am**   **G**
Ref.: And I say: Hey hey hey hey hey hey. I say: „Hey, what's going on?"
                    G   **Am**   **G**
      And I say: Hey hey hey hey hey hey. I say: „Hey, what's going on?"
                Am C
      Uh uh uh   uh

      G
      Twenty-five years and my life is still
      Am   **C**   **G**
      trying to get up that great big hill of hope for a destination. (yeah)

WE WILL ROCK YOU

♩ 84 | Slow Rock

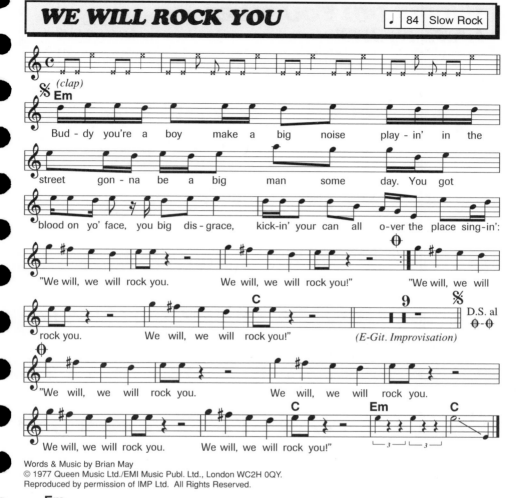

Words & Music by Brian May
© 1977 Queen Music Ltd./EMI Music Publ. Ltd., London WC2H 0QY.
Reproduced by permission of IMP Ltd. All Rights Reserved.

Em
1. Buddy you're a boy make a big noise playin' in the street gonna be a big man some day
you got blood on yo' face, you big disgrace, kickin' your can all over the place, singin':
we will, we will rock you. We will, we will rock you.

Em
2. Buddy you're a young man, hard man shoutin' in the street,
gonna take on the world some day.
You got blood on yo' face, big disgrace, wavin'n your banner all over the place, singin':
                                                  C
we will, we will rock you. *(3x)* We will, we will rock you. *(E-Git. Improvisation)*

Em
3. Buddy you're an old man, poor man pleadin' with your eyes,
gonna make you some peace some day. You got mud on your face, you big disgrace,
somebody better put you back into your place, singin': We will, we will rock you. *(5x)*

              C   **Em C**
we will, we will rock you.

WHERE DID YOU SLEEP LAST NIGHT

| ♩ | 108 | Slow Waltz |

Words & Music by Huddie Ledbetter

1.
    Em   **A**   **G**   **B**   **Em**
  My girl, my girl, don't lie to me. Tell me, where did you sleep last night?
                           A   **G**
  In the pines, in the pines, where the sun don't ever shine,
     B   **Em**
  I would shiver the whole night through.

```
        Em                    A      G      B                        Em
2.  My girl, my girl, where will you go? I'm goin' where the cold wind blows.
                                   A                    G
    In the pines, in the pines, where the sun don't ever shine,
              B                    Em
    I would shiver the whole night through.

        Em                        A      G      B                    Em
3.  The husband was a hard working man, just about a mile from here.
                                   A      G
    His head was found in a driving wheel,
              B              Em
    but his body never was found.

        Em                  A      G          B                      Em
4.  My girl, my girl, don't lie to me. Tell me, where did you sleep last night?
                                   A                    G
    In the pines, in the pines, where the sun don't ever shine,
              B                    Em
    I would shiver the whole night through.

        Em      A      G      B      Em      A      G      B      Em
5.  instrumental

        Em                    A      G      B                        Em
6.  My girl, my girl, where will you go? I'm goin' where the cold wind blows.
                                   A                    G
    In the pines, in the pines, where the sun don't ever shine,
              B                    Em
    I would shiver the whole night through.

        Em                  A      G          B                      Em
7.  My girl, my girl, don't lie to me. Tell me, where did you sleep last night?
                                   A                    G
    In the pines, in the pines, where the sun don't ever shine,
              B                    Em
    I would shiver the whole night through.

        Em                  A      G      B                          Em
8.  My girl, my girl, where will you go? I'm goin' where the cold wind blows.
                                   A          G
    In the pines, in the pines, where the sun don't shine,
              B                    Em
    I would shiver the whole night through.
```

WHISKEY IN THE JAR

♩ 103 | Polka

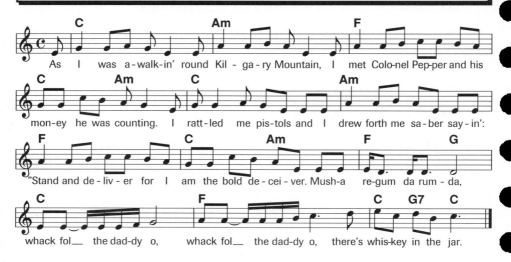

As I was a-walkin' round Kil-ga-ry Mountain, I met Colo-nel Pep-per and his mon-ey he was counting. I ratt-led me pis-tols and I drew forth me sa-ber say-in': "Stand and de-liv-er for I am the bold de-cei-ver. Mush-a re-gum da rum-da, whack fol__ the dad-dy o, whack fol__ the dad-dy o, there's whis-key in the jar.

Traditional aus Irland

1.
    C   **Am**
As I was awalkin' round Kilgary Mountain,
    F   **C**   **Am**
I met Colonel Pepper and his money he was countin'.
    C   **Am**
I rattled me pistols and I drew forth me saber sayin':
    F   **C**   **Am**
"Stand and deliver for I am the bold deceiver."
        F   **G**   **C**
Ref.: Musha regum da rumda, whack fol the daddy o,
        F   **C**   **G7** **C**
whack fol the daddy o, there's whiskey in the jar.

2.
    C   **Am**
The shining golden coins did look so bright and jolly,
    F   **C**   **Am**
I took 'em with me home and I gave 'em to my Molly,
    C   **Am**
she promised and she vowed that she never would deceive me,
      F   **C**   **Am**
but the devil's in the women and they never can be easy. Musha regum ...

3.
    C   **Am**
When I was awakened between six and seven,
    F   **C**   **Am**
the guards were all around me in numbers odd and even;
    C   **Am**
I flew to my pistols, but alas, I was mistaken,
     F   **C**   **Am**
for Molly'd drawn my pistols and a prisoner I was taken. Musha regum ...

```
            C                        Am
4.   They put me in jail without judge or writin'
            F                   C        Am
     for robbing Colonel Pepper on Kilgary Mountain,
            C                           Am
     but they didn't take my fists, so I knocked the sentry down
                        F          C          Am
     and bid a fond farewell to the jail in Slaigo town.  Musha regum ...

            C                        Am
5.   Now, some take delight in fishin' and bowlin'
            F                       C          Am
     and other take delight in their carriages a-rollin',
            C                         Am
     but I take delight in the juice of the barley
            F                          C        Am
     and courtin' pretty girls in the mornin' so early.

                  F            G    C
Ref.: Musha regum da rumda, whack fol the daddy o,
            F                      C     G7    C
      whack fol the daddy o, there's whiskey in the jar.
```

WILD WORLD

♩ 73 | Slow Rock

Words & Music by Cat Stevens
© 1970 Salafa Limited
Sony/ATV Music Publishing (UK) Ltd., 10 Great Marlborough Street, London W1
All Rights Reserved. International Copyright Secured.

```
     Em              A7                    D
1.   Now that I've lost ev'rything to you
                     G                     C
     you say you wanna start something new
                 Am                  B7
     and it's breaking my heart you're leaving. Baby, I'm grievin'!
     Em                    A7               D
     But if you want to leave, take good care,
                       G                    C
     hope you have a lot of nice things to wear,
                 Am                  B7          D7
     but then a lot of nice things turn bad out there.

     G     D              C
Ref.: Oh, baby, baby, it's a wild world.
     D                   C              G
     It's hard to get by just upon a smile.
            D               C
     Oh, baby, baby, it's a wild world.
     D               C              G        Am
     I'll always remember you like a child, girl.

     Em                    A7                            D
2.   You know, I've seen a lot of what the world can do,
                   G               C
     and it's breaking my heart in two
              Am                  B7
     'cause I never want to see you sad, girl, don't be a bad girl.
     Em                    A7              D
     But if you want to leave, take good care,
                      G                    C
     hope you make a lot of nice friends out there,
                 Am                  B7          D7
     but just remember there's a lot of bad and beware.

     G     D              C
Ref.: Oh, baby, baby, it's a wild world.
     D                   C              G
     It's hard to get by just upon a smile.
            D               C
     Oh, baby, baby, it's a wild world.
     D               C              G        Am
     I'll always remember you like a child, girl.

     B7              Em                    A7                 D
     Baby, I love you.    But if you want to leave, take good care,
                      G                    C
     hope you make a lot of nice friends out there,
                 Am                  B7          D7
     but just remember there's a lot of bad and beware.

     G     D              C
Ref.: Oh, baby, baby, it's a wild world ... (fade out)
```

WIND OF CHANGE

♩ 78 | Ballade

I fol-low the Moskva___ down to Gor-ky Park,
listen-ing to the wind of change.___ An Au-gust summer night,
sol-diers pas-sing by,___ listen-ing to the wind of change.___
Take me to the ma-gic of the mo - ment on a glo-
ry night, where the chil-dren of to-mor - row dream a-way,
in the wind of change.___
Take me to the ma-gic of the mo - ment on a glory night, where the chil-dren of to-mor - row dream a-way,
in the wind of change. The wind of change blows straight
in - to the face___ of time,___ like a stormwind that will ring

D.S. al

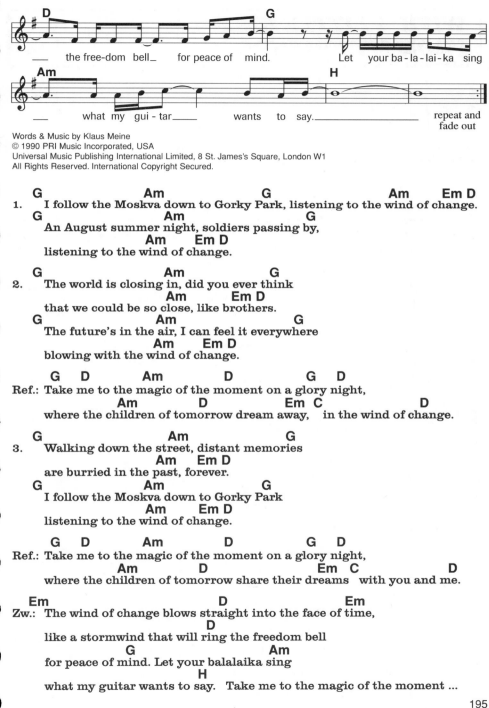

the free-dom bell_ for peace of mind.   Let your ba-la-lai-ka sing

what my gui-tar____ wants to say._____ repeat and
fade out

Words & Music by Klaus Meine
© 1990 PRI Music Incorporated, USA
Universal Music Publishing International Limited, 8 St. James's Square, London W1

      G   Am   G   Am   Em D
1.   I follow the Moskva down to Gorky Park, listening to the wind of change.
    G   Am   G
       An August summer night, soldiers passing by,
             Am   Em D
       listening to the wind of change.

    G   Am   G
2.   The world is closing in, did you ever think
             Am   Em D
       that we could be so close, like brothers.
    G   Am   G
       The future's in the air, I can feel it everywhere
             Am   Em D
       blowing with the wind of change.

      G   D   Am   D   G   D
Ref.: Take me to the magic of the moment on a glory night,
              Am   D   Em C   D
      where the children of tomorrow dream away,   in the wind of change.

    G   Am   G
3.   Walking down the street, distant memories
             Am   Em D
       are burried in the past, forever.
    G   Am   G
       I follow the Moskva down to Gorky Park
             Am   Em D
       listening to the wind of change.

      G   D   Am   D   G   D
Ref.: Take me to the magic of the moment on a glory night,
              Am   D   Em C   D
      where the children of tomorrow share their dreams   with you and me.

Em   D   Em
Zw.: The wind of change blows straight into the face of time,
                       D
      like a stormwind that will ring the freedom bell
           G   Am
      for peace of mind. Let your balalaika sing
               H
      what my guitar wants to say. Take me to the magic of the moment ...

WITH A LITTLE HELP FROM MY FRIENDS

♩ 114 | Shuffle

D   **A**   **Em**   **A**

What would you do___ if I sang___ out of tune,___ would you

Em   **A7**   **D**

stand up and walk___ out on me?___

A   **Em**   **A**

Lend me your ears___ and I'll sing___ you a song___ an I'll

Em   **A7**   **D**

try not to sing___ out of key.___ Oh,___ I get by___

C   **G**   **D**

___ with a lit-tle help___ from my friends.___ Hm,___ I get high___

C   **G**   **D**

___ with a lit-tle help___ from my friends.___ Hm,___ I'm gon-na try

C   **G**   **1. D** **A7**   **2. D**

___ with a lit-tle help___ from my friends.___ friends. Do you need

Bm   **E7**   **D**   **C**   **G**

___ an-y-bod-y?___ I need some-bod-y to love.___ Could it be

Bm   **E7**   **D**   **C**   **G**

___ an-y-bod-y?___ I want some-bod-y to love.___

D.C.
(fade out)

Words & Music by John Lennon & Paul McCartney
© 1967 Northern Songs
All Rights Reserved. International Copyright Secured.

```
        D              A      Em        A
1.  What would you do, if I sang out of tune,
                Em              A7          D
    would you stand up and walk out on me.
                    A           Em          A
    Lend me your ears and I'll sing you a song,
            Em      A7          D
    and I'll try not to sing out of key.

                C               G               D
Ref.: Oh, I get by with a little help from my friends,
                C               G               D
      hm, I get by with a little help from my friends,
                        C           G           D       A7
      hm, I'm gonna try with a little help from my friends.

        D       A       Em          A
2.  What do I do, when my love is away,
            Em      A7      D
    does it worry you to be alone?
                A       Em          A
    How do I feel by the end of the day,
            Em          A7          D
    are you sad, because you're on your own?

                C               G               D
Ref.: Oh, I get by with a little help from my friends,
                C               G               D
      hm, I get by with a little help from my friends,
                    C               G               D
      hm, I'm gonna try with a little help from my friends.

                Bm      E7      D       C       G
Zw.:  Do you need anybody? I need somebody to love.
                Bm      E7      D       C       G
      Could it be anybody? I want somebody to love.

        D           A       Em          A
3.  Would you believe in a love at first sight?
            Em              A7          D
    Yes, I'm certain that it happens all the time.
                    A           Em          A
    What do you see when you turn out the light?
            Em          A7          D
    I can tell you, but I know it's mine.

                C               G               D
Ref.: Oh, I get by with a little help from my friends,
                C               G               D
      hm, I get by with a little help from my friends,
                    C               G               D
      hm, I'm gonna try with a little help from my friends ... (repeat and fade out)
```

WONDERWALL

♩ 86 | Moderato Beat

(3x wdh.)

To - day is gon-na be the day that they're gon-na throw it back to you,___ by now you should've some-how re-al-ised what you got-ta do.___ I don't be-lieve that an - y-bo - dy feels the way I do___ a-bout you now._____

Back-beat the word was on the street that the fi - re in your heart is out.___ I'm sure you've heard it all be-fore but you nev-er real-ly had a doubt. I don't be-lieve that an - y-bo - dy feels the way I do___ a-bout you now.

And all___ the roads we have to walk are wind-ing and all___ the lights that lead us there are blind - ing. There are ma - ny things that I___ would like to say to you___ but I don't know how because may-be_____ you're gon - na be the one that

198

saves me,_____ and af-ter all_____ you're my won-der-wall._

1. A / 2. A F#m

2x D.S.,
2.x al

I said

saves me,_____ you're gon - na be the one that

(7x wdh.)

Words & Music by Noel Gallagher
© 1995 Oasis Music, Creation Songs Limited & Sony/ATV Music.
Publishing (UK) Ltd., 10 Great Marlborough Street, London W1
All Rights Reserved. International Copyright Secured.

F#m   A   E   F#m
Intr.: Today is gonna be the day that they're gonna throw it back to you,
                          A   E   F#m
       by now you should 've somehow realised what you gotta do.
                          A   E   F#m   D E F#m
       I don't believe that anybody feels the way I do about you now.

                          A   E   Bm
1.   Backbeat the word was on the street that the fire in your heart is out.
       F#m   A   E   Bm
       I'm sure you've heard it all before, but you never really had a doubt.
       F#m   A   E   Bm   F#m A E Bm
       I don't believe that anybody feels the way I do about you now.

              D   E   F#m
Ref.: And all the roads we have to walk are winding
              D   E   F#m
      and all the lights that lead us there are blinding.
              D   E   A   F#m
      There are many things that I would like to say to you,
                      Bm   D F#m A
      but I don't know how ,because maybe
              F#m   D   F#m A
      you're gonna be the one that saves me,
          F#m D F#m A   F#m   D F#m A
      and after all   you're my wonderwall.
                          A   E   Bm
2.   Today was gonna be the day, but they'll never throw it back to you.
       F#m   A   E   Bm
       By now you should 've somehow realised what you're not to do.
       F#m   A   E   Bm   F#m A E Bm
       I don't believe that anybody feels the way I do about you now.

              D   E   F#m
Ref.: And all the roads we have to walk are winding ... (fade out)

199

YOU'RE MY HEART, YOU'RE MY SOUL

♩ 117 | Disco Pop

Deep in my heart there's a fire___ burn-in' hard,

deep in my heart there's de-sire___ for a start.

I'm dy-ing in___ e-mo-tion___ it's my

world in fan-ta-sy.___ I'm liv-in' in___ my,

liv-in' in___ my dreams. You're my heart,___ you're my soul,___

___ I'll keep it shin-ing ev'-ry-where I'll go.___ You're my heart,

___ you're my soul,___ I'll be hold - ing you for-e-ver, stay___

___ with you. You're my heart,___ you're my soul___ yeah, I'm
to-geth-er.

feel-in' that our love will grow.___ You're my heart,___ you're my soul,___

___ that's the on-ly thing I real-ly know.___

You're my heart

D.S.
(fade out)

Words & Music by Steve Benson
© 1984 by Hansa Musik Verlag GmbH / Hanseatic Musikverlag GmbH / Blue Obsession Music oHG

    Bm   F#m

1.   Deep in my heart there's a fire burnin' hard,
       Bm   F#m
       deep in my heart there's desire for a start.
           A   Bm
       I'm dying in emotion it's my world in fantasy,
         G   Em   A
       I'm livin' in my, livin' in my dreams.

                  Bm   Em   A   Bm
Ref.: You're my heart, you're my soul, I'll keep it shining ev'rywhere I go.
                                 Em   A
      You're my heart, you're my soul, I'll be holding you forever

      stay with you together.   Bm   G
                        You're my heart, you're my soul yeah,
        A   Bm
      I'm feelin' that our love will grow.
                   G   A   Bm
      You're my heart, you're my soul, that's the only thing I really know.

    Bm   F#m
2.   Let's close the door and believe my burnin' hard,
       Bm   F#m
       feeling alright and you open up your heart.
         A   Bm
       I'll keep the candles burning, let your body melt in mine.
         G   Em   A
       I'm livin' in my, livin' in my dreams.

Ref.: You're my heart, you're my soul ... that's the only thing I really know.

      You're my heart, you're my soul ... *(fade out)*

Die Auswahl der Tonlagen war oft ein Kompromiss, bei welchem wir hohe und tiefe Stimmlagen sowie die Schwierigkeit der Akkorde berücksichtigt haben.
Wer "seine" persönliche Tonart finden will, dem kann die Transponiertafel helfen:

TRANSPONIERTAFEL
Internationale Schreibweise

D# ≅ Eb, G# ≅ Ab, C# ≅ Db, F# ≅ Gb
Das B (intern. Schreibweise) wird in unserem nationalen Buchausgaben als H bezeichnet. das Bb als B.

Tonart Dur	Moll	Vor-zei.											
Des	b	5 b	Gb	Db	Ab	Eb	Bb	F	C	G	D	A	E	B
As	f	4 b	Db	Ab	Eb	Bb	F	C	G	D	A	E	B	Gb
Es	c	3 b	Ab	Eb	Bb	F	C	G	D	A	E	B	Gb	Db
B	g	2 b	Eb	Bb	F	C	G	D	A	E	B	Gb	Db	Ab
F	d	1b	Bb	F	C	G	D	A	E	B	Gb	Db	Ab	Eb
C	a	-	F	C	G	D	A	E	B	F#	C#	G#	D#	Bb
G	e	1 #	C	G	D	A	E	B	F#	C#	G#	D#	Bb	F
D	h	2 #	G	D	A	E	B	F#	C#	G#	D#	Bb	F	C
A	fis	3 #	D	A	E	B	F#	C#	G#	D#	Bb	F	C	G
E	cis	4 #	A	E	B	F#	C#	G#	D#	Bb	F	C	G	D
H	gis	5 #	E	B	F#	C#	G#	D#	Bb	F	C	G	D	A
Fis	dis	6 #	B	F#	C#	G#	D#	Bb	F	C	G	D	A	E

Beispiel:
Ein Lied ist in F-Dur angegeben, aber einige schaffen die höchsten Töne nicht.
Hier bietet sich vielleicht D-Dur an.
Also sucht man alle Töne in der Zeile F-Dur drei Zeilen tiefer in der Zeile D-Dur genau in der gleichen Spalte. B wird zu G, C wird zu A ...

So können auch Jodlerinnen und Brummbären mitsingen!

Was bedeutet: C/G
Das G nach dem Schrägstrich ist der zum Akkord gehörige Basston, welcher dem Akkord seine besondere Klangfarbe gibt.
„Normale" Gitarristen spielen hier nur den Grundakkord C. Ebenfalls nur für Geübte sind die Alterationen (Veränderungen) der Akkorde, z.B. C9, F5+.
Auch hier kann der „Normalgitarrist" mit dem Grundakkord auskommen.

BoE 7015

Hit-Kiste

Das superstarke Songbook
mit 120 tollen Oldies, unvergänglichen Top-Hits,
weltbewegenden Songs und Liedern
und beliebten Mitsing-Schlagern
von gestern und heute

A Whiter Shade Of Pale
Blowing In The Wind
Bridge Over Troubled Water
Crocodile Rock
Ein Bett im Kornfeld
Hard Day's Night
Hey Jude
Lady In Black
Love Me Tender
Marmor, Stein und Eisen bricht
Michelle
Morning Has Broken
99 Luftballons

New York, New York
No Woman No Cry
Pretty Woman
Rivers Of Babylon
Rock Around The Clock
Sag mir, wo die Blumen sind
San Francisco
Spanish Eyes
Waterloo
We Are The World
Yesterday
Your Song
...und viele andere mehr!!!

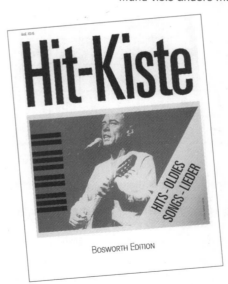

BOSWORTH EDITION

Made in the EU. 4/03 (47423)